IAN BLACK is wee, fat and extremely nippy when Glasgow's good name is impugned by people who know little or nothing of this most magnificent of cities. He's in his 50s now and has the scars to prove it. He likes Glaswegians, though, and has the scars to prove that too, as well as memories of warmth, unthinking generosity and largeness of spirit from the melange of people who make up the Glaswegian population.

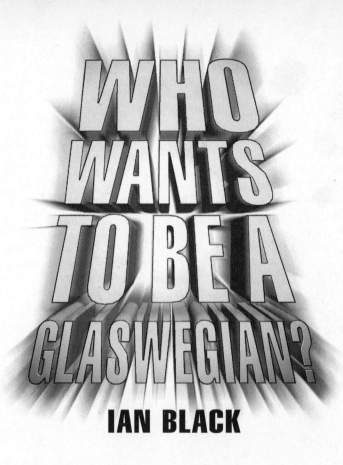

WHO WANTS TO BE A GLASWEGIAN?

IAN BLACK

Black & White Publishing

First published 2002
by Black & White Publishing Ltd
99 Giles Street, Edinburgh EH6 6BZ

ISBN 1 902927 35 4

A CIP catalogue record for this book is available from
The British Library.

Printed by Omnia Books Ltd, Bishopbriggs

Contents

Introduction

The answers to the rhetorical questions asked in the song 'Who Wants To Be A Millionaire' are always negative, though most Glaswegians would say: 'Aye, me,' when asked any of them. I mean, who doesn't want to wallow in champagne, or fly a supersonic plane? I certainly do, and you won't find many negative answers or even negative questions in the tome you are now holding in your hand, though there is one which at a late stage in the book's production more or less posed itself, and it is: 'Why does Chapter 1 have 60 questions and all of the others only 50?' Choose one from these answers:

a) It is an attempt to establish that having to think duodecimally sharpens the intellect, thereby increasing the readers' chances of actually becoming a Glaswegian.

b) The author is the numerical equivalent of a dyslexic and a numpty. And just to be negative for a moment, the answer is not a).

You may also notice that a few of the questions are not about Glasgow. This is because Glaswegians have a DNA-driven propensity to know everything about everything in the world. Don't fight it, it's a genetic thing.

There are, however, many positive things about wanting to become a Glaswegian – things like finally understanding what we are talking about and maybe even getting some of the jokes, of which there are usually more than a few in any conversation between Glaswegians. Glasgow is a sort of city-state of mind and most of us are Glaswegians first and Scots next – which of course means that the sense of humour is both broad, self-deprecating and ironic. It is also as black as five yards up a chimney.

Try this on your friends. A guy goes to a door and, when the woman of the house appears, asks: 'Is Wullie in?' The woman lets loose a sob and says: 'Have ye no' heard, John? Wullie fell into a vat of molten steel this morning and got burnt to death.' John pauses for a moment and says: 'Jeez. Did he say anything about a can of paint?'

If you laughed at that, you are well on your way to understanding the mindset. Honest to God, people from Edinburgh do not laugh at this joke. Neither do Americans. I use it as a kind of litmus paper test of people. Jewish people laugh at it and so do Liverpudlians. Belfast people love it, London people look at you in horror.

This book is a bit like that. I hope you do become a Glaswegian. You'll be welcome.

THE QUESTIONS

> 'The past is a foreign country; they do things differently there.'
>
> L. P. Hartley

1

History

You can't set a test on Glasgow's history without mentioning the rest of Scotland, so that's it mentioned. Let's get on with the real stuff.

As the Monty Python team had it in *The Life of Brian*: 'So the Romans gave us roads, sanitation and a legal code. What else have they done for us?' The answer, in Glasgow, would be nothing. Not even those three. When they left the Clyde, they left nothing but the odd remnant. No roads, no bridges, no settlements. It stayed that way too for centuries, until a punter called Kentigern came from the East – like wise men do – looked upon the land and found it good, though God knows why. Maybe he was a drumlin fancier, as modern Glasgow is built on and from these heaps of Ice Age rubble.

Kentigern changed his name to Mungo, as you do if you have left Fife in a hurry, and built a church on a drumlin beside the Molindinar Burn. That site is now occupied by Glasgow Cathedral, parts of which date from the 12th century, and Mungo is now Saint Mungo, a man who, to save a woman caught in adultery, ordered a Clyde-caught salmon to cough up a ring. This tale is commemorated, along with other legends attached to his name, in the Glasgow coat of arms, which has a fish, a ring, a bell and a tree.

That was back in the sixth century. Mungo must have been a pretty charismatic guy for a saint, as next thing you know he and his church were surrounded by farmers, millers, shepherds, fishermen and lots of people who just came to see him levitate while preaching – an uncommon skill back then as it still is, despite the claims of those yogi eejits you see on the box.

Fast-forward six hundred years to when another bishop, Jocelyn, a Cistercian, got the budding city a charter from the King of Scotland, Big Wullie the Lion. This gave it permission to trade as a unit, and a sort of government – run by Jocelyn and his mates – came into being.

Jocelyn also got the King to grant permission for a fair, which is still recognised 800 years later as the Glasgow Fair. Times have changed a bit, but in living memory this fair meant a virtual shut-down for the city, and the entire country tilted to the West as the citizens of Glasgow decamped Doon the Watter.

There is still a Fair on Glasgow Green in July, although it is no longer possible or permissible to buy bears or some of the less mentionable bits of St Anthony – more's the pity, as these bits were a sure cure for ergotism, a gangrenous disease brought about by eating bread affected by fungus.

There were other diseases too, including several visits from the Black Death. 'Hello, I'm the Black Death, can I come in?'

But the city avoided famine and by 1451 or so had acquired a university – still on the go and, rumour has it, still with many of the same lectures, professors and teaching methods.

By the middle of the next century Glasgow was trading with the Baltic ports, France and Holland, and some time after the Union of the Crowns in 1603 the city was starting to make serious profits from the American colonies, yee-hah! This caused the English parliament to enact protection laws, a direct cause of the Darien disaster in which about 2500 people died in a failed attempt at setting up a Scottish colony on the Isthmus of Panama. It nearly ruined the city financially, but by the time the 'parcel of rogues' sold Scottish nationhood for English gold with the Union of the Parliaments in 1707, Glasgow was more than ready for equal trading status and huge fortunes were made from sugar, tobacco and the old yo-ho-ho and a bottle of.

Once Port Glasgow was established, it was possible to sail to the Americas in 10 or 11 days less than it took from London, and it was this that started shipbuilding on the Clyde. Though the yards are mostly peopled by ghosts now, the traditions remain. The Clyde built the world's first commercial steamship, Henry Bell's *Comet*, and sent forth in pride the great Cunarders like the *Queen Elizabeth*, the *Queen Mary* and the *QE2*, as well as vast tonnages of more mundane craft.

Maggie and her minions then tried to kill Glasgow off by shutting down all her industries, and in the last 50 years Glasgow has suffered more body blows than Rocky Balboa. But like Rocky we are still standing here. Our city is the cleanest it has ever been, we have more parks than any city in Europe, some of the finest museums and art galleries in Britain, world-famous architecture and an inbred belief that nobody owes us a living. Our universities and colleges still attract many more students than they have room for and education is one of the fastest growing industries.

Tourism is another, and the bestowing of the title of European City of Culture in 1990 opened a few eyes – not least our own – to the fact that a lot of what we take for granted – like being the home of Scottish Ballet, Scottish Opera and the Royal Scottish National Orchestra, not to mention the two best football teams in Scotland – is really a bit special, just as we are.

So, who wants to be a Glaswegian? You think you are that good? Come ahead then.

1.1 Glasgow is on . . . ?

a	Drugs	c	The Forth
b	The Clyde	d	The Fifth

1.2 Kentigern changed his name to . . . ?

a	Daft Sandy	c	Mungo
b	Mongo the Monkey	d	Ming the Merciless

1.3 Where was he from originally?

a	Fife	c	Oldmeldrum
b	Edinburgh	d	Newmeldrum

1.4 What is a drumlin?

a	A wee drum	c	A fish
b	A heap of Ice Age rubble	d	A rumbling advertisement

1.5 What had to disgorge a ring?

a	Neptune	c	Richard Wagner
b	Madonna's husband	d	A Salmon (not Alex)

6

1.6 What else is on Glasgow's coat of arms?

a	A bell	c	A tree
b	A ring	d	All of these

1.7 What did Mungo do while preaching?

a	Salivate	c	Micturate
b	Levitate	d	Speculate

1.8 What order of monks did Jocelyn belong to?

a	Sisters of Mercy	c	Great apes
b	Cistercians	d	Trappists

1.9 When is Glasgow Fair?

a	All the time	c	July
b	When it likes	d	August

1.10 What is ergotism?

a	Saying, 'Therefore!' too much	c	A gangrenous disease
b	Bigheadedness	d	A love of fungus

1.11 When was the Union of the Crowns?

a	When Thomas met Sally	c	When Bobo met Coco
b	1603	d	1707

1.12 Where is Darien?

a	Panama	c	Nicaragua
b	In an Oz soap	d	Austria

1.13 When was the Union of the Parliaments?

a	1707	c	1706
b	1708	d	1999

1.14 Name a commodity from America which enriched Glasgow.

a	Chewing gum	c	Rum
b	Nuclear missiles	d	Madonna

1.15 Name a Cunarder built on the Clyde.

a	*Cooee Two*	c	*QE2*
b	*Cooee Won*	d	*QE3*

1.16 What was the world's first commercial steamship called?

a	*B&Q*	c	*Jesus Christ Superstar*
b	*Comet*	d	*Makro*

1.17 Name a growing industry in Glasgow?

a	Tourism	c	Tourism
b	Tourism	d	Wishful thinking

1.18 In what year was Glasgow European City of Culture?

a	1951	c	1877
b	1988	d	1990

1.19 Name the best football team in Glasgow?

a	Celtic	c	Partick Thistle Nil
b	Rangers	d	Queens Park

1.20 What does RSNO stand for?

a	Royal Scottish National Orangemen	c	Royal Scottish National Orchestra
b	Rich Snotty Naff Outsiders	d	Rich, Sam, Nat, Oliver

1.21 Who painted *Christ of St John of the Cross*?

a	Dilly	c	Delay
b	Dalai Lama	d	Dali

1.22 Who bought it for Glasgow?

a	Tom Honeyman	c	Pastor Jack Glass
b	Julian Spalding	d	Elspeth King

1.23 When?

a	1951	c	1953
b	1952	d	Yonks ago

1.24 How much did it cost?

a	Too much	c	£2,800
b	Not enough	d	£8,200

1.25 Who sang 'The Wee Cock Sparra'?

a	Joel MacRae	c	Drunken MacRae
b	Duncan MacRae	d	MacRae of Sunshine

1.26 Name a movie he was in?

a	*Whisky Galore*	c	*Bad Day at Black Rock*
b	*Titanic*	d	*The Maggie*

1.27 Another one?

a	*Local Hero*	c	*Geordie*
b	*Comfort and Joy*	d	*That Sinking Feeling*

1.28 And another?

a	*Tunes of Glory*	c	*The Glory Guys*
b	*The Glory Game*	d	*Gloria*

1.29 Name Scotland's first World Boxing Champion?

a	Chic Calderwood	c	Dick MacTaggart
b	Walter MacGowan	d	Benny Lynch

1.30 Which area of Glasgow was he from?

a	Polmadie	c	Bridgton
b	Gorbals	d	Kelvinside

1.31 What age was he when he died?

a	33	c	34
b	32	d	35

1.32 Where is the only statue of Shakespeare in Glasgow?

a	In Shakespeare Street	c	The Citizen's Theatre
b	The Tron Theatre	d	The Theatre Royal

1.33 What is the animal that is part of the statue in Woodlands Road?

a	A two-legged horse	c	A four-legged horse
b	A three-legged horse	d	A one-legged horse

1.34 What is her name?

a	El Fideldo	c	El Filedlo
b	La Fidelda	d	La Filedlo

1.35 Why, if she is female, does she have a male name?

a	She's a transvestite	c	It's a mistake
b	Her folks wanted a wee boy horse	d	Sexism

1.36 Name the Sheriff on her back?

a	Dobey Losser	c	Jobby Tosser
b	Lobey Dosser	d	Tobby Josser

1.37 And the villain?

a	Bank Rajin	c	Tank Bajin
b	Rank Bajin	d	Yank Bajin

1.38 When was Queens Park founded?

a	Who cares?	c	1869
b	1867	d	1872

1.39 When was the first Scotland v. England International?

a	1872	c	1869
b	1867	d	1872

1.40 Where was it played?

a	Mount Florida	c	Ibrox
b	Partick	d	Maryhill

1.41 How many Queens Park players played in that game?

a	8	c	10
b	9	d	11

1.42 What was the score?

a	0–0	c	1–0
b	7–0	d	0–7

1.43 What is Queens Park nicknamed?

a	The Webs	c	The Fly Men
b	The Spiders	d	The Bully Wee

1.44 Why is Bath Street so called?

a	It was only open on Friday nights	c	They baked buns there
b	After the English town	d	Glasgow's first public baths were there

1.45 Who, in Glaswegian terms, is Lazarus?

a	Do Lally	c	Da Lally
b	Pat Lally	d	Pot Lally

1.46 What is the title of his autobiography?

a	*Lazarus Only Tried It Once*	c	*Lazarus Only Tried It Twice*
b	*Lazarus Only Done It Once*	d	*Lazarus Only Done It Twice*

1.47 Why doesn't Pat Lally have a knighthood?

a	He turned it down	c	He's too nice
b	He doesn't deserve one	d	Only the Labour Party knows

1.48 What cost a halfpenny to cross in 1853?

a	The Jamaica St Bridge	c	The Railway Bridge
b	The Suspension Bridge	d	The Erskine Bridge

1.49 How many tons of garnets were taken from Garnethill?

a	None	c	Two
b	One	c	Three

1.50 Who is sitting on the big equestrian statue outside the Gallery of Modern Art?

a	Lord Boot	c	Lord Sandal
b	Lord Wellington	d	Lord Deckshoe

1.51 Why does he have a traffic cone on his head?

| a | It's funny | c | He's double-parked |
| b | It suits him | d | Students |

1.52 What are the dark-clothed and intense young people outside the Gallery of Modern Art called?

| a | Vandals | c | Goths |
| b | Visigoths | d | Peter and Jane |

1.53 And the ones with the wheeled planks?

| a | Skiteboarders | c | Jane and Peter |
| b | Shiteboarders | d | Skateboarders |

1.54 What were the special golden seats at Green's Playhouse called?

| a | Love Seats | c | Sofas |
| b | Divans | d | Sofa so good |

1.55 How was it pronounced?

| a | Divan | c | Deevan |
| b | Dive-on | d | Deevon |

1.56 Who wrote 'I Belong to Glasgow'?

a	Jimmy Logan	c	Will Fyffe
b	Harry Lauder	d	Tommy Morgan

1.57 Who won the Booker Prize for a novel set in Glasgow?

a	Tom Leonard	c	Jim Kelman
b	Liz Lochead	d	Ian Black

1.58 What was the first stage play Billy Connolly appeared in?

a	*The Terrible Northern Welly Boot Show*	c	*The Great Western Welly Boot Show*
b	*The Great Northern Welly Boot Show*	d	*The Terrible Western Welly Boot Show*

1.59 What was the first stage play Billy Connolly wrote?

a	*Jobbies, Farts and Willies*	c	*This is Me since Yesterday*
b	*Me wi' a Bad Leg Tae*	d	*The Coos'll Get Ye*

1.60 When did Queen Street station open?

a	1842	c	1852
b	1832	d	1862

2

Attitude, Language and the Patter

'Yer patter's like watter. Ye can see right through it.'

Anon,
but definitely Glaswegian

The first line of one of Willie MacIlvanney's books, *The Papers of Tony Veitch*, is 'Glasgow. Friday night. The city of the stare'. And it can be. But it is also the city of the stairheid, the sair heid and of the patter. We're quick, we are, and some of us are sharp enough to cut ourselves. We are also sometimes a little surreal. Dave Anderson tells a tale of being on a bus to Garthamlock. (Told you it was surreal.)

One of the passengers, who had been badly over-served in a bar in the city centre, took it upon himself to entertain his fellow passengers. As he is eight bars into 'Your Cheatin' Heart', the bus swerves and deposits him on his bot in the aisle, clunking his head in the process. As Dave offered to help him up,

the wee man (you rarely see a big drunk in Glasgow) says to the company at large:

'Just leave us tae Garthamlock. If ye waant, gie us a rub-doon wi' a can a soup. If yez are feelin kinky, make it cockaleekie.'

Dave swears that this is true and further attests, vis-à-vis the strangeness of Glaswegians, that he has seen a piece of graffiti in a loo which said: 'Real Madrid – 2, Surreal Madrid – fish'.

Gerard Kelly, Dave's sparring partner in the much-loved and much-missed *City Lights*, tells of shooting a scene outside a job centre in Parkhead. They are up to take number umpty, it is getting late and tensions are running high. There are 17 people concentrating on a square yard in front of the broo when into it steps a wee man intent on getting to the job centre. As the lights hit his eyes he looks up, does a double then a treble take at all the lights, cameras, action etc. and, before anyone can shout at him, says, 'Whit's a' the kerry-oan? Somebody get a joab?'

And it is catching, the patter. An Asian bus conductor on the late night service to Easterhouse had to turn away two aggressive young men as there was only one space on the bus and they wouldn't separate. The next in the queue jumped on the bus and one of the young men said to the conductor, 'You can stick your bus up your arse!' The conductor smiled gently and said, 'Sir, if you could have done that with your friend, you could both be on my bus.'

Glaswegians do not suffer fools gladly. Pretension and pomposity have no bigger enemies than your average Glaswegian, if there is such a person, and the one-liner and the sharp put-down have been honed to a razor-edged art form. Bill Paterson, the ex-Dennistoun actor, tells of working part-time in a bar there. It was a slow afternoon and the talk turned to the ineffable mysteries of life, as it does on a slow afternoon in Dennistoun. There was talk of Zen, Confucianism, Christian dogma and the great imponderables of existence. One of the group kept asking, 'Why are we here? Why are we here?' and repeated it so many times that Wullie, the ancient sage in the bunnet in the corner, raised his head and said, 'Davie, you're here because it wis

Hogmanay and yer faither was on leave fae the army. Yer ma telt me.'

The last census here established that 74 per cent of the population of Glasgow thought that they could be funnier than Billy Connolly, given the chance, while 17 per cent thought that they were already funnier than Billy Connolly. The other 9 per cent thought that they were Billy Connolly.

Billy tells a tale of a superintendent in a shipyard where he used to work enquiring of a worker, 'Do you know who I am?' in that self-important manner which raises hackles and sometimes fists in Glasgow. The welder looked at him askance and said to his mate, 'Hey, Peter, here's a guy wi' amnesia.'

There is also a warmth here to go with the sharpness. We think nothing of accosting a stranger with a bandaged head, or sometimes even a Sikh, with the question, 'Are you looking for Aikenhead Road?' One Sikh replied, 'Don't gie us any of your patter. Ahm wan a thae turban guerillas.' And who of us has not been addressed in the pub, bus or subway by a bloke indicating himself with that unique two-handed gesture and saying, 'This is me since yesterday'? Who of us has been spinning a line of fanny to two German journalists about it being a bye-law in Glasgow that you have to name your eldest son Jimmy, simply because they were being arrogant assholes, and been interrupted by a lawyer, complete with gown, who quoted chapter and verse, including the bye-law number? Or was that just me?

The journalists printed the story and the lawyer, whom I didn't know previously, and I still buy each other the odd pint.

When you are standing in a pub in Edinburgh, chatting idly with to your nearest neighbour, as you do, have you ever had the dawning realisation that the ghastly rictus on his face means that he is standing there thinking, 'What does this wee Glasgow guy want?', when all you want is some human contact, a bit of banter? If you have, you should sail through these next questions. They are about attitudes, language and the *mot juste*.

2.1 What is a dobber?

a	A variety of Australian grass	c	A Celtic word for a Rangers supporter
b	An indifferent A-less painter	d	A howling eejit

2.2 What is the best answer to the question, 'Is it yersel?'

a	'Yes'	c	'No'
b	Who's askin?	d	Silence

2.3 What is the best response to the question, 'A Billy or a Dan or an auld tin can?'

a	'A Billy'	c	'An Auld tin can'
b	'A Dan'	d	Flight

2.4 Who or what is the Magnificent Seven?

a	A movie with Clark Gable	c	Henrik Larsson
b	James Caan	d	A movie with 3¹/₂ Dolly Partons

2.5 Complete this phrase, 'Gonny no . . .'

a	'Please'	c	'Pee in ma pint'
b	'Dae that'	d	'Stop'

2.6 And then?

a	'Jist no gonny'	c	'No jist gonny'
b	'Gonny no jist'	d	'Jist gonny no'

2.7 Who are you if you are not Hairy Mary?

a	Hirsute Harry	c	Furry Murray
b	Yer Maw	d	Shaven Sheila

2.8 Who sang of 'Cod Liver Oil and the Orange Juice'?

a	Matt McGinn	c	Hamish Imlach
b	The NHS	d	Ewan McVicar

2.9 Who sang of 'Three Nights and a Sunday'?

a	Hamish Imlach	c	Matt McGinn
b	Shop stewards	d	Trainee doctors

2.10 And the phrase after Sunday?

a	Time and a half	c	And I'm cream crackered
b	Treble time	d	Double time

2.11 Matt McGinn used to sing of a 'big Effen bee'. Where is 'Effen'?

a	In France	c	In Germany
b	In Fife, near Ecclefechan	d	Effen nowhere

2.12 Where is John Maclean buried?

a	Eastwood Cemetery	c	Westwood Cemetery
b	Northwood Cemetery	d	Southwood Cemetery

2.13 Who wrote the song 'My Ain Close'?

a	Matt McGinn	c	Duncan Macrae
b	Morris Blythman	d	Hamish Imlach

2.14 What is a moony?

a	A Korean cult member	c	A bare bum
b	A slow dance	d	A crazed person

2.15 If you give someone the message, what are you doing?

a	Battering lumps out of them	c	Handing over groceries
b	Passing information	d	Kneading their flesh

2.16 What is a minder?

a	An associate of George Cole	c	A thinking person
b	A small gift	d	A rememberer

2.17 What is a 'Trannie'?

a	A male dressed as a female	c	A small radio
b	A female dressed as a male	d	A Transcard

2.18 Joe Baxi is . . . ?

a	An Argentinian	c	A phonetical loss of employment
b	A black cab	d	A drink

2.19 'Gregories' are . . . ?

a	A series of popes	c	Spectacles
b	Girls	d	Chants

2.20 What is a 'meringue'?

a	A crumbly confection	c	A dance
b	Glaswegian for 'Am I correct?'	d	French for 'meringue'

2.21 'Baggies' are . . . ?

| a | Police cars | c | Sacks |
| b | Small fish | d | Claims |

2.22 'Mee-maws' are . . . ?

| a | Police cars | c | Hawaiian clothing |
| b | Aggravating children | d | A terrorist organisation |

2.23 A 'huvtae' case is . . . ?

| a | A tea chest | c | A forced marriage |
| b | A schoolbag | d | A need to go to the toilet |

2.24 A snotter is . . . ?

| a | Nasal mucilage | c | The lower support of the spirit |
| b | Someone who continuously disagrees | d | Part of a horse's fetlock |

2.25 What is a 'riddie'?

| a | A district of Glasgow | c | A puzzling question |
| b | Embarrassment | d | A flour-sifter |

2.26 Who is not the 'full shilling'?

| a | A woman called Bo | c | A hat designer |
| b | Anyone who can't answer this | d | A man with eleven pence |

2.27 'Acme wringers' are ... ?

| a | Very useful | c | Left wingers |
| b | Fingers | d | Right wingers |

2.28 Who or what in Glasgow is 'steak and kidney'?

| a | A nutritious pie filling | c | A pretence |
| b | Sydney Devine | d | A large sword |

2.29 What is put in lager to make a shandy?

| a | Lime | c | Water |
| b | Legal Aid | d | Coke |

2.30 What are the 'Harry Wraggs'?

| a | Cigarettes | c | Harold's clothing |
| b | Partick Thistle | d | A famous jockey |

2.31 Who is on the 'hey diddle diddle'?

a	The cat	c	A swindler
b	The fiddle	d	Someone in the toilet

2.32 A 'crossmyloof' is . . . ?

a	A skating rink	c	A hybrid sponge
b	A male homosexual	d	A pub

2.33 What is small, brown and furry and swims out to sea shouting, 'Fuck the Pope?'

a	A bitter lemming	c	A bitter apple
b	A bitter orange	d	A bitter lime

2.34 Who wrote the song 'As Soon as This Pub Closes, the Next Revolution Begins'?

a	Alex Dundee	c	Alex Edinburgh
b	Alex Glasgow	d	Alex Aberdeen

2.35 What is a 'hudgie'?

a	A Glasgow school	c	A lift
b	A house for rabbits	d	A thing for constraining people

2.36 Who is last to turn up for work?

a	A 'skitterysummer'	c	A 'skitteryspring'
b	A 'skitteryautumn'	d	A 'skitterywinter'

2.37 What are you if you are 'gas-cookered'?

a	Burnt	c	Roasted
b	Boiled	d	Snookered

2.38 What happened to the man who ate bricks?

a	He left	c	He's awa' noo
b	He's gone now	d	He has departed

2.39 Who are the Glasgow Eskimos?

a	Rangers supporters	c	CND Supporters
b	Celtic Supporters	d	Partick Thistle supporters

2.40 Where did the hardman come from?

a	Oot o' the West	c	Oot o' the North
b	Oot o' the East	d	Oot o' the South

2.41 What colour was Matt McGinn's whale?

a	Orange	c	Purple
b	Blue	d	Gold

2.42 Which granny can you shove off a bus?

a	Your mother's maternal parent	c	A draught excluder for chimneys
b	Your father's maternal parent	d	A knot

2.43 Which half of the Humblebums did Billy Connolly say he was?

a	The Humble one	c	The Sad one
b	The Proud one	d	The Happy one

2.44 Where was 'I Belong to Glasgow' first performed?

a	The Pavilion	c	The Empire
b	The Scotia	d	The Metropole

2.45 R.S. McColl, the sweetie shop founder, played for?

a	Celtic	c	Clyde
b	Queens Park	d	Partick Thistle

2.46 What was a 'leerie'?

a	A man who took LSD	c	A scaredy cat
b	A lamplighter	d	A lewd smiler

2.47 What is a 'wally close'?

a	A stupid ending	c	The end of a wall
b	A tiled common entrance	d	A tiled toilet

2.48 Who or what are the 'Tim Malloys'?

a	Celtic Football Club	c	Empty teacakes
b	An Irish family	d	Blended metals

2.49 What or who are the 'Teddy Bears'?

a	Picnickers	c	Loveable soft toys
b	Rangers Football Club	d	Naked people called Edward

2.50 'Geezabrek' is . . . ?

a	Esperanto	c	An appeal to desist
b	A breakfast cereal	d	A tea break

3

'There is no tradition of
theatre in Scotland.'

Gerry Mulgrew

'Bollocks'

Ian Black

Theatre and
Music Hall

Theatre in Glasgow has a long history. The first recorded performance was on 4 August 1763. It was a performing flea and it was a shilling to see it, a fortune in those days. A wifie from the Shaws saw the flea and killed it instinctively, wiping out the entire cast with her thumbnail – something many people in Glasgow wish they could do, particularly to Scottish soaps and those dreadful No.5 Touring Company shows from England. It is not recorded what the Professor (people who run flea circuses are always called 'Professor') said or did, but you can be pretty sure he would have been hopping mad.

From there the Penny Geggies developed in and around Glasgow Green. There were often just paper screens between them and they were room- rather than theatre-size. They didn't just cost a penny, except in the very beginning. It often cost as much as sixpence, but for that you could get to see Johnny Parry. His act was called The Deid Man's Drap and consisted of Johnny coming on, falling off a fake cliff and dying. This was the whole act and he was apparently so good at playing dead that doctors were called on several occasions to revive him.

Fast forward a hundred or so years to the Bursts, where the establishment gave you a poke with buns, cakes, etc. If you liked the act you blew up your bag and burst it, hence 'Bursts'. Then came the music halls. There is a tale told of the kindly proprietor of the Scotia Music Hall in Stockwell Street giving Harry Lauder his first chance. Harry didn't feel it had gone all that well and he was standing hangdog, waiting to be sent back down the pits, when the lady gave him his minuscule fee, patted his cheek and said, 'There you are, my boy. Now go home and practise.' Which, as we know, he did. Of such small gestures are national stereotypes and the future of Scottish music hall made.

Fast-forward another hundred years to now, where all of the strands of theatre in Glasgow have intermingled and entwined in interesting and unexpected ways. It may cost more than a penny, and the word 'geggie' only heard in the phrase, ' Shut your geggie!', but theatre remains a vibrant part of Glasgow culture. The word eclectic is not an all-embracing enough description of theatre in Glasgow and neither is broad, multifaceted or wide ranging. Because not only do Glasgow's theatres and its companies cover the entire spectrum but they – and the huge number of companies based here – make regular and successful attempts to expand that spectrum.

One of the most successful and the most spectacular is Tramway. That's 'Tramway' not 'The Tramway' or 'Tramway Theatre'. Pretentious, *nous*? *Pas de tout*. It is a home away from home for the elfin-faced adopted Glaswegian Peter Brook, whose production of *The Mahabarata* kick-started Tramway's career as a performing space in a manner that can only be described as astounding.

Critics came from all parts of the world and, most satisfyingly, from those two

most provincial of cities, London and Edinburgh, to be mesmerised and astounded. French-Canadian *wunderkind* Robert Lepace is also a Tramway aficionado and his production there of *Tectonic Plates* will be remembered for ever by anyone who was privileged to see it.

We seem to be good at turning odd spaces into theatres and we must be unique in Britain for having two theatres where trains run on a regular basis under, over or beside them. They are The Tron and The Arches, which has all of Central Station overhead. The noises at The Tron so intrigued and amused a visiting Russian director that he incorporated them into the text of the play and, every time a train went past, the actors dived and pressed their ears to the floor. The Arches has just had a major refurbishment and more of Andy Arnold's work, like *Metropolis* and *The Crucible*, is eagerly anticipated.

The Citizen's need no further praise and its three performance spaces turn out works of quality that seem to get better with every season, while the Theatre Royal, as well as being the premiere theatre for Scottish Opera and Scottish Ballet, acts as a receiving theatre for the most prestigious companies in Britain, and the King's does the same for musicals.

There are lots more companies producing work in spaces around the city but final mention must be made of The Pavilion, the last bastion of demotic theatre in Glasgow. It does everything from touring hypnotists to tribute bands and its home-grown efforts are a continuing joy.

Theatre is not only alive in Glasgow, it is positively bursting with a vibrant good health – so much so that it decamps to Edinburgh *en masse* in August to give the Edinbuggers a transfusion of new blood, not to mention guts. Imagine a whole city getting drunk and waking up with a Tattoo.

3.1   Where is the Pavilion?

| a | Renfrew Street | c | Renfield Street |
| b | Brighton | d | Far away |

3.2   Where is the King's?

| a | Sauchiehall Street | c | Buried on Iona |
| b | Buckingham Palace | d | Bath Street |

3.3   Where was The Empire?

| a | All over the world | c | Sauchiehall Street |
| b | Just the pink bits | d | A biscuit factory |

3.4   Where or what is The Tron?

| a | A computer game | c | The last bit of a mello |
| b | The Trongate | d | George Square |

3.5   Where or what is The Arches?

| a | A boring radio programme | c | Under the Heilanman's Umbrella |
| b | Two ventriloquist's dolls | d | Under your feet |

36

3.6 Where is the Theatre Royal?

a	Buckingham Palace	c	Brighton
b	Hope Street	d	In the Royal Family

3.7 Who or what is the Mitchell?

a	A guy	c	A library
b	A woman	d	A German with Michelle off *EastEnders*

3.8 What is Tramway?

a	A thing trams run on	c	A road in Toronto
b	An arty space on the South Side	d	A road in Rome

3.9 Who or what is the Citizen's?

a	A theatre in the Gorbals	c	The folk
b	The people	d	People who aren't standing

3.10 Where was *The Mahabarata* performed?

a	Calcutta	c	Theatre Royal
b	Tramway	d	King's

3.11 In which Glasgow theatre can you hear trains?

a	The King's	c	The Tron
b	The Pavilion	d	The Citizen's

3.12 And another one?

a	Tramway	c	The King's
b	The Arches	d	The Pavilion

3.13 And a former one?

a	The Empire	c	The Old Athenaeum
b	The Scotia	d	The Empress

3.14 How many square feet are there in the Arches?

a	12,000	c	15,000
b	1200	d	1500

3.15 Name a play produced at the Arches?

a	*Metropolis*	c	*Gotham City*
b	*City*	d	*Tube City*

3.16 Where is the Ramshorn?

| a | On the Ramshead | c | In Ingram Street |
| b | Between the Ram's legs | d | In Albion Street |

3.17 How much was a 'penny geggie'?

| a | A penny | c | Thruppence |
| b | Tuppence | d | Fourpence |

3.18 Where was the Alhambra?

| a | In Canada | c | Stockwell Street |
| b | At the corner of Waterloo Street | d | Mexico City |

3.19 When did the Empire open?

| a | 1897 | c | 1899 |
| b | 1895 | d | 1893 |

3.20 Who topped the bill?

| a | Marie Lloyd | c | George Lashwood |
| b | Vesta Tilley | d | Tom Costello |

3.21 The new Empire opened in 1931. Who topped that bill?

a	Jack Payne's Band	c	Billy Bennett
b	A. C. Astor	d	Rose du Barry

3.22 Who or what was Rose du Barry?

a	A singer	c	The colour of the Empire's upholstery
b	A dancer	d	A comic

3.23 Which of these did not appear at the Empire?

a	Laurel and Hardy	c	Bob Hope
b	Abbot and Costello	d	Gene Autry

3.24 When did the Empire close?

a	1963	c	1964
b	1962	d	1965

3.25 When did the Alhambra open?

a	1910	c	1912
b	1911	d	1417

3.26 And close?

| a | 1969 | c | 1968 |
| b | 1970 | d | 1967 |

3.27 Who topped the closing bill?

| a | Cilla Black | c | The Merseybeats |
| b | Gerry and the Pacemakers | d | Jimmy Logan |

3.28 Where was the Britannia Music Hall?

| a | Saltmarket | c | The Broomielaw |
| b | Trongate | d | Stockwell Street |

3.29 Who took it over in 1906?

| a | Albert E. Einstein | c | Albert and Victoria |
| b | Albert E. Pickard | d | Jorg Albertz |

3.30 What did he call it?

| a | The Plainoptician | c | The Optpanicon |
| b | The Panopticon | d | The Brittania Music Hall |

3.31 When did the Coliseum open?

a	1981	c	1931
b	1905	d	1932

3.32 What did the Great Carmo make vanish at the Coliseum?

a	A lion	c	The audiences
b	The smell	d	The architect

3.33 Who was the architect?

a	Charles Rennie Mackintosh	c	Greek Thompson
b	Frank Matcham	d	Solomon

3.34 There was a riot between an illusionist and medical students there in 1909. What was it called?

a	The Bodie Riot	c	The Baddie Riot
b	The Clergyman Riot	d	The Sterrheid Stushie

3.35 Whose catchphrase was, 'Sausages is the boys'?

a	Denny Willis	c	Walls
b	Jimmy Logan	d	Andy Stewart

3.36

What was Jimmy Logan doing at the Metropole from 1964–71?

a	Topping the bill	c	Footing the bill
b	Taking the tickets	d	Running the bar

3.37

Whose catchphrase was, 'Ahl get ye! Ahl get ye!'

a	Tommy Lorne	c	Tommy Morgan
b	Denny Willis	d	Lex McLean

3.38

If he didn't get ye, what got ye?

a	The giraffes	c	The bulls
b	The coos	d	The squirrels

3.39

Mark Sheridan flopped on stage at the Coliseum and took a tram to Kelvingrove Park. What did he do there?

a	Had a nice walk	c	Shot himself
b	Smelled the flowers	d	Threw himself in the Kelvin

3.40

What makes the Pavilion unique in Britain?

a	Its manager is baldy	c	Its shows are often crap
b	It has a sliding roof	d	It has a ghost

3.41 Who were the last two actors onstage at the Empire?

a	Duncan Macrae and Albert Finney	c	Duncan Macrae and Laurence Olivier
b	Duncan Macrae and Yootha Joyce	d	Duncan Macrae and Alex Norton

3.42 What did they do?

a	A soft-shoe shuffle	c	Took pickaxes to the stage
b	The Tintock Cup	d	Sang 'Scotland the Brave'

3.43 How long did *Hair* run at the Metropole?

a	38 weeks	c	The same as the rabbits
b	About 12 inches	d	48 weeks

3.44 Which James Bond has appeared at the Citizen's?

a	Sean Connery	c	George Lazenby
b	Pierce Brosnan	d	Roger Moore

3.45 What colour does Giles Havergal wear on first nights?

a	Blue	c	Beige
b	Brown	d	Black

3.46 What, according to Giles, do you do if you balance the books?

| a | Not pay actors enough | c | Not pay him enough |
| b | Buy freedom | d | Buy him champagne |

3.47 When did Giles join the Citz?

| a | Before the Flood | c | 1962 |
| b | Just after it | d | 1963 |

3.48 What play opened the Citz season in 1970?

| a | *Macbeth* | c | *Hamlet* |
| b | *King Lear* | d | *Romeo and Juliet* |

3.49 Where did *The Scotsman* print its review of this play?

| a | In a centre spread | c | On the front page |
| b | On the back page | d | In a specially issued supplement |

3.50 Who wrote it?

| a | Allen Wright | c | Christopher Large |
| b | Christopher Small | d | Allen Wrong |

> 'For vivacity and agility in dancing, none excel the Scotch ladies.'
> Edward Topham, 1776

> 'I just watch the feet of the best dancers in the hall.'
> Jimmy Shand on his timing

4

The Dancin'

If it wasn't for the dancin' and the romances that this most pleasant of ways to meet the opposite sex engendered, most of us wouldn't be here. In the '20s, as well as the 12 big, dressy-up ballrooms, there were another 80 or so on the go, from local halls to district ones. You learned in the small ones – and you had to learn, as being a bad dancer was a social stigma beyond imagining these days – and then you graduated to the bigger ones.

Apart from the boy-meets-girl thing, if you were any good, you could make a good living from demonstrating and teaching the new dances. When the Charleston arrived in Glasgow in 1923, its demonstrators, Mills and Siele, were paid more than £100 a week, an absolute fortune in those days. One of them,

Annette Mills, went on to a different kind of dancing fame, as she was the string-puller for Muffin the Mule in the early days of steam television.

These halcyon days are, of course, past, but in the past they must not necessarily remain. Clubs have replaced the big halls, but the reasons for going remain valid. Boy meets girl – or, nearly as frequently these days, boy meets boy and girl meets girl – is as good a reason as any for going out. The dancing skills may not be as finely honed, but there are new skills, like recognising bad Es, lip-reading or dressing like the undead.

These questions are not for the young. You'll need to ask your mum, your dad, or your grandparents for at least some of the answers. Get them to talk about the dancin'. They'll tell you stuff you didn't

47

know and they may even get all teary-eyed on you. Nostalgia is not, of course, as good as it was but it is still most excellent fun for young and old, just like the dancin'.

4.1 How many major ballrooms were there in Glasgow in the '20s?

a	12	c	15
b	107	d	7

4.2 And in Edinburgh?

a	None	c	1
b	12	d	5

4.3 What does that suggest?

a	Edinbuggers are joyless tubes	c	Glasgow is bigger then Edinburgh
b	A difference of 7	d	All of these

4.4 When did the Charleston first arrive in Glasgow?

a	1923	c	1928
b	1924	d	1929

4.5 Who first demonstrated it?

a	Mills and Siele	c	Harper and Ross
b	Mills and Boon	d	Ross and Harper

4.6 What was Annette Mills' claim to fame?

a	She was related to John Mills	c	She was the Mills in Mills and Boon
b	She was one of the Carnwath Mills	d	She wrote *Oklahoma*!

4.7 And another?

a	She manipulated Muffin the Mule	c	She could tap dance on her hands
b	She invented the Black Bottom	d	She once ate a whole lamb

4.8 What did the sign 'PCQ' on ballroom walls mean?

a	'Please Clogdance Quickly'	c	'Puff Cigarettes Quickly'
b	'Please Charleston Quietly'	d	'Pull Cigarettes Quietly'

4.9 Who taught the then Prince of Wales to Charleston?

a	His mum	c	Beryl Evetts
b	His dad	d	His nanny

4.10 What was different about the Hibs dancehall in Garngad?

a	The women wore clogs	c	Both sexes were barefoot
b	The men danced with their caps on	d	The women were barefoot

4.11 When did the Greens Playhouse Ballroom open?

a	1928	c	1931
b	1929	d	1932

4.12 How many springs did the floor have?

a	None	c	10,000
b	1000	d	10

4.13 In the'30s what was the alfresco style of dancing in the streets called?

a	Clubber dancing	c	Clibber dancing
b	Clabber dancing	d	Clobber dancing

4.14 What was Glasgow's own dancing style called?

a	Select dancing	c	Sand dancing
b	Choice dancing	d	Picky dancing

4.15 Joe Loss played a four-week booking at the Greens at Christmas 1940. How many customers paid in the first week?

a	1000	c	7000
b	3000	d	10,000

4.16 How many more Christmas seasons did he play at the Greens?

a	Until 1950	c	Until 1967
b	Until 1957	d	Until 1961

4.17 Which of these is not a dance?

a	'The Dashing White Sergeant'	c	'The Emperor's Tango'
b	'Gypsy Tap'	d	'Blues Breakaway'

4.18 When did the Dennistoun Palais open?

a	1938	c	1940
b	1939	d	1941

4.19 What is it now?

a	A supermarket	c	A disco
b	A library	d	A butchers

4.20 Which is the correct answer to the question, 'Ur ye dancin?'

a	'Ur ye askin?'	c	'Yes, thank you'
b	'Naw, it's jist the wey ahm staunin'	d	All of these

4.21 In two weeks in 1932, how many people took rumba tuition at the Greens?

a	None	c	100
b	1000	d	500

4.22 What do you do first in the 'Hokey Cokey'?

a	You put your right leg in	c	You put your right hand out
b	You put your right leg out	d	You put your right hand in

4.23 How old was Louis Freeman when he played his last gig?

a	75	c	89
b	79	d	99

4.24 How old was Louis when he died in 1994?

a	101	c	105
b	107	d	103

4.25 What year did the Barrowland Ballroom open?

a	1933	c	1935
b	1934	d	1936

4.26 Whose idea was it?

a	The stallholders at the Barras	c	Joss Loss
b	Mrs Margaret McIver	d	Billy McGregor

4.27 Name the first resident band?

a	The Gayboys	c	The Gaylords
b	The Gaybirds	d	The Gaymen

4.28 What was unique about the Plaza?

a	The fountain	c	The band
b	The bouncers	d	The dancers

4.29 When did Joe Loss stop coming to the Plaza?

a	1937	c	1980
b	1957	d	1990

4.30 Why did he stop?

a	He couldn't moonwalk	c	Disco happened
b	He died	d	He discovered acid

4.31 Which Glasgow dancehall did Lord Haw Haw mention?

a	The Albert	c	The Dennistoun Palais
b	Barrowland	d	The Plaza

4.32 Why?

a	He had danced there	c	He was a champion dancer
b	Their neon sign	d	He was looking for a lumber

4.33 In 1939 what did you need to gain entry to a Glasgow ballroom?

a	A dinner suit	c	A gas mask
b	A uniform	d	Tuppence

4.34 Who said in 1941, 'It seems appalling that men, face-to-face with the realities of eternity, should be regaled with dance music'?

a	Lord Haw Haw	c	Hitler
b	King George VI	d	The Lord's Day Observance Society

4.35 Where did you jitterbug in the Barrowland?

a	Jitterbug Alley	c	Jitterbug Street
b	Jitterbug Lane	d	Jitterbug Wynd

4.36 The practice of walking someone home from the dancing is called?

a	A timber	c	A lumber
b	Pining	d	A limber

4.37 What major film used the Barrowland as a location?

a	*Ebbtide*	c	*High Tide*
b	*Floodtide*	d	*Low Tide*

4.38 Farquar Macrae managed the Berkeley Ballroom in the early '50s. What was his nickname?

a	Flash	c	Ajax
b	Tide	d	Surf

4.39 Name the Plaza's formation dancing team?

a	The Moonlight Formation	c	The Sunlight Formation
b	The Starlight Formation	d	The Daylight Formation

4.40 Who coined the term 'rock and roll'?

a	Alan Freeman	c	Alan Freed
b	Bill Haley	d	Elvis Presley

4.41 Where in 1961 was Geordie's Byre?

| a | Near Geordie's farm | c | The Locarno |
| b | Barrowland | d | The Albert |

4.42 What did The Locarno become?

| a | Melanie's | c | Sexy Sadie's |
| b | Tiffany's | d | Saucy Sue's |

4.43 What did it become next?

| a | A shoe warehouse | c | A casino |
| b | A cinema | d | An Indian restaurant |

4.44 Which serial killer will always be associated with the Barrowland?

| a | Bible John | c | Peter Manuel |
| b | Jungle Jim | d | Ted Bundy |

4.45 Where was the only Scottish appearance of Bill Haley?

| a | The Odeon Cinema | c | Green's Playhouse |
| b | Barrowland | d | The Pavilion |

4.46 And the year?

a	1963	c	1962
b	1964	d	1965

4.47 The Scottish dancing stars named Irvine are . . . ?

a	Joe and Janette	c	Bill and Bobby
b	James and Jim	d	James and Joe

4.48 And the couple called Burns and Fairweather are . . . ?

a	Rabbie and There's Always	c	Bill and Annie
b	Donnie and Gaynor	d	John and Janet

4.49 Which football ground was the Lorne Ballroom part of?

a	Ashfield	c	Parkhead
b	Ibrox	d	Hampden

4.50 When did Barrowland close for dancing?

a	1971	c	1973
b	1972	d	1974

5

Art, Culture and That

> 'Art is the flower – life the green leaf . . . there are things more precious – more beautiful, more lasting than life.'
> Charles Rennie Mackintosh

A visitor to Edinburgh could be forgiven for asking, 'So you are the capital? Where is the National Orchestra, the National Ballet, the best theatre company, the BBC's orchestra and the best art collections and gallery in Scotland?' He could also be forgiven for saying, 'Ah, so you have the Parliament building. It is going to cost how much!!' The two exclamation marks here denote a bat-like screech of incredulity. The same screech goes with, 'And house prices have doubled!!' It is now widely accepted by Scottish society that siting the Parliament in Edinburgh was a Glaswegian ploy to keep house prices down here and to relocate tubes, rogues and carpetbaggers eastward to their spiritual home.

There are more than 250 performing arts organisations in Glasgow and the numbers grow each year, despite the parsimony of the Scottish Arts Council and the Government's anti-art attitude. On any one evening there are more than 12,000 seats available for opera, theatre and ballet – though not often the latter two on the same night, as they are both based in the Theatre Royal – and for listening to music in any of the dozens of spaces – some terrific, some good, some just this side of terrible.

The Apollo – the quintessentially down-and-dirty home of that greasy and exciting devil's music, the rock and the roll – has gone, but have you seen the size of its replacement? We are talking big here, as we do, and quite often it turns out to be true.

Who Wants to be a Glaswegian?

We've got the Big Red Shed, The Armadillo, the first of which has played host to Dylan, The Eagles, Michael Jackson and hundreds of other megastars, not to mention Pavarotti and Carreras. The acoustics are terrible, but what the hell, it's only rock 'n' roll, even when it's opera.

Then there's the Concert Hall, from the Albert Speer school of architecture. It is officially known as Glasgow Royal Concert Hall but everybody calls it the Concert Hall, including the Royal Scottish National Orchestra, who play there on a regular basis, as do the BBC Scottish Symphony Orchestra, the Glasgow Phoenix Choir, Call That Singing? and more rising (and fading) pop and musical stars than you could shake a stick at. If your taste runs to the visual arts, then you are in the right place. The much-vilified Wee Jules Spalding did a good job on GOMA, our latest gallery, which is even popular with Goths – not to mention skateboarders, who are to be found in hordes around it.

A few years back the city fathers rather belatedly came to the conclusion that officially vandalising and/or destroying the work of our most famous architect, Charles Rennie Mackintosh, was (oops!) an error of judgement and have now got around to promoting him. Glasgow School of Art is his most famous work and there are daily organised tours. If you like it – and you will – pop up the road to Queens Cross Church in Maryhill Road, which is a small and perfectly faceted gem of a building, worth travelling a country mile to see.

On the Soo Side there's the Burrell Collection, a brilliant building set in parkland and a celebration of the jackdaw – like acquisition skills of Sir William Burrell. What do you get a man who collects Rodins, Rembrandts and castle doorways for his Christmas? There is also Kelvingrove and St Mungo, which celebrates all aspects of religion – not something we are normally renowned for – plus the People's Palace – which rhymes with gallus – which is what it is, an eclectic collection of nostalgic ephemera much beloved by our citizens.

See art? See Glasgow?

5.1 What is the difference between Sir Alexander Gibson and a Radox foot bath?

a	There is none	c	A Radox foot bath bucks up your feet
b	The bath is bubblier	d	Sir Alex was bubblier

5.2 In what year did Scottish Opera start?

a	1962	c	1947
b	1963	d	1948

5.3 It opened with what?

a	*Aida*	c	*The Magic Flute*
b	*The Ring*	d	*Madame Butterfly*

5.4 Name a character in *Madame Butterfly*.

a	Cio Cio San	c	Cio Cio Sim
b	Ciao, ciao son	d	Cio Cio Sun

5.5 Who wrote it?

a	Benjamin Britten	c	Verdi
b	Puccini	d	Mozart

5.6 Who conducted this performance?

a	Sir Alexander Gibson	c	Leon Lovett
b	Roderick Brydon	d	Norman Del Mar

5.7 Where is Scottish Opera based?

a	The King's	c	Glasgow Royal Concert Hall
b	Theatre Royal	d	Edinburgh

5.8 Where was their first performance?

a	The King's	c	Glasgow Royal Concert Hall
b	Theatre Royal	d	Edinburgh

5.9 Name a chamber opera of Benjamin Britten?

a	Albert Herring	c	The Turn of the Cooler
b	Bismarck Herring	d	Pickled Herring

5.10 What secondary school did Sir Alexander Gibson attend?

a	Dalziel High, Motherwell	c	The High School for Boys
b	Low Dalziel, Motherwell	d	Hutcheson's Grammar

5.11 What did he conduct for his first professional engagement?

a	*The Battered Bride*	c	*The Buttered Bride*
b	*The Battered Bridie*	d	*The Bartered Bride*

5.12 By . . . ?

a	Holst	c	Smetana
b	Mozart	d	Britten

5.13 Who performed the British premiere of *Idomeneo*?

a	The Glasgow Grand Opera Society	c	The Opheus Choir
b	The Grand Ole Opry	d	Father Sydney MacEwan

5.14 *Idomeneo* is by . . . ?

a	Berlioz	c	Mozart
b	Puccini	d	Smetana

5.15 Mary Garden was . . . ?

a	A soprano	c	An alto
b	A bass	d	A counter tenor

5.16 Where is Edinburgh Opera House?

a	There isn't one, ha ha	c	The Assembly Rooms
b	The Royal Lyceum	d	Edinburgh King's

5.17 Where was Father Sydney MacEwan born?

a	Kelvinside	c	Springburn
b	Gorbals	d	Possil

5.18 Where was his first paid performance?

a	St Paul's	c	The Vatican
b	Millport	d	Dunoon

5.19 How much was he paid?

a	£408	c	£25
b	£500	d	Seven shillings and sixpence

5.20 What instrument did Orpheus play?

a	A flute	c	A clarinet
b	A lute	d	A dulcimer

5.21 When was the Glasgow Orpheus Choir formed?

a	1922	c	1905
b	1923	d	1906

5.22 When was the current Scottish Ballet formed?

a	1969	c	1965
b	1970	d	1966

5.23 Where did they first make an appearance in Glasgow?

a	Theatre Royal	c	Pavilion
b	King's	d	Citizen's

5.24 In . . . ?

a	*Romeo and Juliet*	c	*Paquita*
b	*The Trojans*	d	*Beauty and the Beast*

5.25 With music by . . . ?

a	Mozart	c	Berlioz
b	Prokofiev	d	Vivaldi

5.26 Under the artistic direction of . . . ?

a	Peter Darrell	c	Stuart Hopps
b	Ashley Killar	d	John Newmeier

5.27 Who danced Andromache in Part 1?

a	Graham Bart	c	Elaine McDonald
b	Hazel Merry	d	Dame Margot Fonteyn

5.28 When did Sir Alexander Gibson join the SNO?

a	1988	c	1963
b	1959	d	1964

5.29 Whom did he succeed?

a	Swarowsky	c	Karl Muck
b	Rankl	d	Herbert von Karajan

5.30 When did the St Andrews Halls burn down?

a	1962	c	1963
b	1961	d	1969

5.31 When were the City Halls built?

a	1841	c	1831
b	1851	d	1861

5.32 Who succeeded Sir Alex at the SNO?

a	Neeme Jarvi	c	Karl Muck
b	Herbert von Karajan	d	Sir John Barbirolli

5.33 Who wrote the symphony *From the New World*?

a	Chopin	c	Dvořák
b	Liszt	d	Brahms

5.34 Who wrote *The Blue Danube*?

a	Brahms	c	Johann Strauss II
b	Richard Strauss	d	Dick Advocaat

5.35 Who wrote *Ode to Joy*?

a	Ludwig van Beethoven	c	Bill Travers
b	Hertz van Rental	d	Schubert

5.36 When did Mozart write *The Marriage of Figaro*?

a	1786	c	1776
b	1796	d	1787

5.37 What was Franz Haydn's middle name?

a	Schioklegraber	c	Heinz
b	Joseph	d	David

5.38 And Handel's first two?

a	John Frederick	c	George Joseph
b	George Frideric	d	Frederick George

5.39 And Bizet?

a	Georges	c	Jörg
b	Geordie	d	Izzy Wizzy

5.40 What's the name of the Bizet opera about the gypsy and the soldier?

a	*Miranda*	c	*Carmen*
b	*Carmen Miranda*	d	*Carmel*

5.41 Where did Chopin play in Glasgow?

a	The City Halls	c	The Concert Hall
b	The Merchants' Hall	d	The Kelvin Hall

5.42 Name one of the things represented by the statues outside the Mitchell Theatre?

a	*Paperwork*	c	*Victory*
b	*Science*	d	*Underwater basket weaving*

5.43 Where is the only known medieval image of St Mungo?

a	Glasgow Cathedral	c	The People's Palace
b	Glasgow City Chambers	d	Cologne Cathedral

5.44 Who created *She Who Was Once the Beautiful Haulmiere*?

a	Peter Howson	c	Eduard Bersudsky
b	Rodin	d	Giacometti

5.45 Who painted the portrait of Alexander Reid in Kelvingrove?

a	Peter Howson	c	Van Gogh
b	Ken Currie	d	Picasso

5.46 Where is *She Who Was Once the Beautiful Haulmiere*?

a	The Uffizi	c	The Louvre
b	The Vatican	d	The Burrell

5.47 Name Glasgow's recent war artist?

a	Ken Currie	c	Peter Howson
b	Adrian Wiszniewski	d	Douglas Thompson

5.48 Which has the funniest newspaper diary in Scotland?

a	*The Scotsman*	c	*The Press and Journal*
b	*The Herald*	d	*The Dundee Courier*

5.49 When did the Gallery of Modern Art open?

a	1996	c	1995
b	1997	d	1990

5.50 Which artist created the Sharmanka Gallery in Glasgow?

a	John Taylor	c	John Bellamy
b	Eduard Bersudsky	d	John Byrne

6

Football

When you talk about sport in Glasgow most people assume you mean football. And by football they mean Celtic and Rangers, the two teams who have brought both fame and shame to Glasgow in large measures. The fame resides in the recognition of the names of the teams in faraway places. The word 'Glasgow' is usually repeated, accompanied by an upward jabbing thumb and the word 'Rangers' or 'Celtic'. The shame is in the bigotry which has blighted the game in Glasgow virtually from the foundation of both clubs. It is not the malignantly powerful force that it was, though small poisonous reservoirs remain, like abscesses requiring lancing.

But the rivalry these days is mostly about who can make the best jokes about the opposition. Digs like, 'How can you tell that Freddy Kruger is a Rangers supporter?', to which the answer is, 'He looks like one', are regularly updated and are of course interchangeable, one of the enduring and recurring joys of life in Glasgow.

They have each won nine championships in a row, though the story is that you can tell it is September in Glasgow because both teams are out of Europe. This season will no doubt be different. Both teams have invested heavily in recent years in new stadia, not to mention players, and both are seeking new fields to conquer – or at least to lose in – in England.

Both brands – because nowadays that is what they are – have a way to go before they reach Man. U. proportions but,

71

what with the worldwide Celtic and Rangers diaspora and the ever-increasing satellite coverage, they might just make it. They have of late hugely increased the entertainment quotient of football in Glasgow and both sides and their supporters – especially their supporters – believe themselves to be on their way to where every Glaswegian believes his or her team to be: at the top of every league, and possessor of every piece of soccer silverware in the known universe. If there is life on Mars – which there certainly is in Glasgow, especially on Saturdays – then perhaps a Rangers/Celtic select could be organised to play a friendly match, though supporters of both teams have been quoted as saying, 'We don't play friendlies.'

Team loyalties run deep and go back generations. Both grounds, Parkhead and Ibrox – or Celtic and Rangers, green and blue respectively, if you are actually from Mars – receive dozens of requests each year to have the ashes of supporters scattered on the terraces or the turf of their preferred team's stadium. You can go on tours round both, though it might be a good idea to conceal the souvenirs obtained at the first ground before visiting the second. Sectarian rivalries may have dimmed, but tongues are sharp and friendly malice abounds.

There are, of course, other teams in Glasgow, quite literally thousands of them, including Partick Thistle – promoted in 2000/1 and heading for glory (maybe just) – and also a quaint and much-loved hangover from the days when football was a game for gentlemen rather than players. They are Queens Park, the only amateur team in Britain still playing in the professional leagues. Their nickname is the Spiders, and like Robert the Bruce's spider, they keep try, try, trying again.

Maybe this millennium will be kinder, and maybe Billy Connolly will be forgiven his jibe about the Jags, as Partick Thistle are known: 'Until I was 24 I thought they were called Partick Thistle Nil.' Don't hold your breath, though.

6.1 What is a friendly nickname for Rangers?

a	The Dobs	c	The Teddy Bears
b	The Blues	d	The Greens

6.2 And for Celtic?

a	The Tim Malloys	c	The Blues
b	The Taigs	d	The Greens

6.3 And for Clyde?

a	The Big Bullies	c	The Wee Bully
b	The Wee Bullies	d	The Bully Wee

6.4 And for Partick Thistle?

a	The Jaggies	c	The Jags
b	The Jiggies	d	The Jigs

6.5 Who won the Scottish Cup in the 1998/9 season?

a	Celtic	c	Hearts
b	Rangers	d	Motherwell

6.6 And in the 2000/1 season?

a	Celtic	c	Hearts
b	Rangers	d	Motherwell

6.7 And in the 1990/1 season?

a	Celtic	c	Hearts
b	Rangers	d	Motherwell

6.8 And in the 1951/2 season?

a	Celtic	c	Rangers
b	Hearts	d	Motherwell

6.9 And in the 1905/6 season?

a	Rangers	c	Hearts
b	Celtic	d	Motherwell

6.10 And in 1873/4?

a	Third Lanark Volunteer Rifles	c	Queens Park
b	Clydesdale	d	Renton

6.11 Who did they beat?

a	Clydesdale	c	Third Lanark Volunteer Rifles
b	Vale of Leven	d	Renton

6.12 What was the score?

a	7–1	c	2–0
b	4–0	d	6–0

6.13 Who beat Celtic 8–0 in 1937?

a	Motherwell	c	Aberdeen
b	Rangers	d	Dunfermline

6.14 Who beat Rangers 10–2 in 1886?

a	Airdrie	c	Celtic
b	Vale of Leven	d	Dunfermline

6.15 Who are the Gable Endies?

a	Albion Rovers	c	Montrose
b	Berwick Rangers	d	Cowdenbeath

6.16 And the Blue Brazil?

a	Albion Rovers	c	Brechin
b	Berwick Rangers	d	Cowdenbeath

6.17 Queens Park are nicknamed?

a	The Diddies	c	The Arachnids
b	The Amateurs	d	The Spiders

6.18 And Stirling Albion?

a	The Dandies	c	The Girls' Own
b	The Beanos	d	The Stirling

6.19 And Stranraer?

a	The Red Lichties	c	The Red
b	The Blue Lichties	d	The Blue

6.20 And Forfar?

a	The Pants	c	The Lunatics
b	The Loons	d	The Ath

6.21 Who are the Wasps?

a	White Anglo-Saxon Protestants	c	Ross County
b	Alloa	d	Stenhousemuir

6.22 Name Airdrie's last opponents in Europe?

a	Dukla Prague	c	Sparta Prague
b	Dukla Pumpherston	d	Sparta Pumpherston

6.23 Six foot-two, eyes of blue. Who is after you?

a	Big John Holton	c	Big Yogi Bear
b	Big Jim Holton	d	The Big Yin

6.24 Who are the Honest Men?

a	Football Agents	c	Ayr United
b	Falkirk	d	Queen of the South

6.25 And the Doonhamers?

a	Queen of the South	c	Berwick Rangers
b	Stenhousemuir	d	Ross County

6.26 Who has scored most goals for Rangers?

a	Sam English	c	Jimmy Millar
b	Ally McCoist	d	Ralph Brand

6.27 And in a season?

a	Sam English	c	Jimmy Millar
b	Ally McCoist	d	Ralph Brand

6.28 Who scored most goals for Celtic in a season?

a	Joe McBride	c	Kenny Dalgleish
b	Jimmy McGrory	d	Charlie Nicholas

6.29 Where do Ajax play?

a	The Amsterdam Arena	c	The Amsterdam de Meer
b	The Rotterdam Arena	d	The Rotterdam de Meer

6.30 And Eindhoven?

a	Philips Stadion	c	Rotterdam Stadion
b	John's Stadion	d	Pieters Stadion

6.31 In the 1891/2 season who were beaten 20–0 by Johnstone in the Scottish Cup?

a	Greenock Imbibers	c	Greenock Morton
b	Greenock Abstainers	d	Greenock Moderates

6.32 In the 1984/5 season who beat Selkirk 20–0?

a	Celtic	c	Stirling Albion
b	Rangers	d	East Stirlingshire

6.33 Who was the second player to be sent off in a Scottish Cup Final?

a	Roy Aitken	c	Jock Stein
b	Andy Paton	d	John Gregg

6.34 What did it cost to get in to the first Scottish Cup Final?

a	Thruppence	c	Fivepence
b	Fourpence	d	Sixpence

6.35 What was Willie Waddell's nickname?

a	The Hun	c	Wee Willie
b	Deedle Dawdle	d	Big Wullie

6.36 And Jimmy Johnstone's?

a	Blinky	c	Kinky
b	Jinky	d	Skinnymalinky

6.37 Who scored for Scotland at Ibrox against Sweden in 1996?

a	Billy Dodds	c	John McGinlay
b	John Collins	d	Paul McStay

6.38 What hills can you see from Stenhousemuir's ground?

a	The Mendips	c	The Campsies
b	The Ochils	d	The Grampians

6.39 What can you see at East Fife's ground?

a	A Bay	c	The Ochils
b	A Cove	d	A Park

6.40 And what can you see at Dumbarton's ground?

a	A Bog	c	A Bay
b	A Toilet	d	A Cove

6.41 Which Dickens character sound like a Celtic fan?

| a | Bob Cratchitt | c | Tiny Tim |
| b | Mr Gradgrind | d | David Copperfield |

6.42 And which historical conqueror sounds like a Rangers fan?

| a | Charlemagne | c | Alexander the Great |
| b | Attila the Hun | d | Julius Caesar |

6.43 Which Roman emperor was Billy McNeil?

| a | Nero | c | Caesar |
| b | Augustus | d | Gregory |

6.44 What game sounds like it is played at Montrose's ground?

| a | Rugby | c | Badminton |
| b | Golf | d | Hockey |

6.45 Who said, 'All I know most surely [of life] I owe to football'?

| a | Derek Johnstone | c | Kevin Keegan |
| b | Albert Camus | d | Kenny Dalglish |

6.46 Which football stadium's name means 'dungheap'?

a	Ibrox	c	Pittodrie
b	Parkhead	d	Brockville

6.47 Who scored the winning goal in the Centenary Cup Final in 1973?

a	Tom Forsyth	c	John Brown
b	John Gregg	d	Derek Parlane

6.48 When Rangers lose 1–0 at Ibrox, who misses the penalty?

a	Barry Ferguson	c	Whoever takes it
b	Lorenzo Amoruso	d	Dick Advocaat

6.49 Why do the Tartan Army hate Jimmy Hill?

a	He is English	c	He is an over-opinionated old fart
b	He said Narey's goal was a 'toepoke'	d	Fill in own answer

6.50 'He's bald, he's fat, he's gonny get the sack . . .' What is the next word?

a	Brown	c	O'Neill
b	Advocaat	d	Davies

7

Sport that Isn't Football

There is a lot of football in Glasgow. But there is also a lot of other sport, both for playing and for endlessly discussing, and there is also a lot of interest in sport worldwide. If you ask, or even assert your own view, you will receive an opinion on everthing from sumo wrestling to fly-fishing in Sumatra. (A large number of our citizens, incidentally, are not sumo wrestlers. They just look that way. If you wish to emulate them, the secret ingredient is chips.)

If you are into sport, tennis, badminton and squash, clubs abound and there are sports and leisure centres within easy reach in most areas. There's good quality rugby, too, and athletics of the national and international kind at both Kelvin Hall International Sports Arena and Crownpoint Sports Park, where you can watch or use the facilities, including five-a-side (football again), weightlifting, table tennis, hockey, a climbing wall and plethora of step, aerobic and keep-fit classes. There are also swimming pools all over the place, unless you live in Govanhill.

And there's golf. There is a little-known bye-law in Scotland that you are not allowed to build a city, town, village or even largish hamlet without its quota of golf courses – both municipal and private. All of them welcome visitors, though you should phone ahead in any event as they tend to get busy over the summer.

If all this hasn't worn you out and you like water – which is obligatory here, as we've got so much of it that it occasionally falls from the skies – then you can try your hand at canoeing, diving in Firhill Basin or you could even hie yourself down to the bonny, bonny banks for a multiplicity of wet and windy activities, like water skiing, windsurfing, sailing or even powerboating. You can fish if you like too, and if you don't like, you can watch Paul Young doing it on TV. When twitted about his obsession, Paul says, 'I've fished for my country. What have you done?' It is not just his hooks that are sharp.

There is also – hold the front page – news of a petanque club starting up. This is also called 'boules', and there is another game with the same pronunciation but a different spelling – 'bools' – which you have to become proficient at before becoming a Glaswegian. Moshie, anyone?

7.1 Who won the 2001 Open Golf Championship?

a	Colin Montgomery	c	Gary Player
b	Ian Woosnam	d	David Duval

7.2 Who was the last Scot to captain the British Lions?

a	Mike Campbell-Lamerton	c	Gordon Brown
b	Andy Irvine	d	Sandy Carmichael

7.3 Who won a gold medal in the 1972 Olympics despite falling?

a	David Broom	c	Chris Chataway
b	Lasse Viren	d	Emil Zatopek

7.4 Who was the Olympic champion who played a gay in *Soap*?

a	Bob Seagren	c	Bob Greensea
b	Bob Seagreen	d	Bob Seegren

7.5 Who was the first player to appear for three different teams in the European Cup?

a	Kevin Keegan	c	Maradona
b	Gordon Smith	d	Louis Figo

7.6 What do Kevin Keegan's first three internationals have in common?

a	They were all against Wales	c	They were all against Scotland
b	They were all against Ireland	d	They were all against Northern Ireland

7.7 When did Alex Higgins win his first world title?

a	1973	c	1972
b	1974	d	1976

7.8 Who beat him the following year in the semis?

a	Eddie Charlton	c	Terry Griffiths
b	Jimmy White	d	Doug Mountjoy

7.9 What was Bob Seagren's gold medal for?

a	Pole-vaulting	c	Long jumping
b	High jumping	d	Hurdles

7.10 Who was the first left-hander to win Wimbledon twice?

a	Yvonne Goolagong	c	Rod Laver
b	Jimmy Connors	d	John McEnroe

7.11 Who knocked holders Celtic out of the European Cup in the first round in 1968?

a	Leeds	c	Dinamo Kiev
b	Ajax	d	Feyenoord

7.12 Who was first to compile an official 147 at snooker?

a	Fred Davis	c	Ray Rearden
b	Joe Davis	d	John Pulman

7.13 Which snooker player carried the Olympic torch in 1956?

a	Joe Davis	c	Willie Thorne
b	Eddie Charlton	d	Perrie Mans

7.14 Which English rugby player appeared as a replacement against Scotland in 1976 and never played for them again?

a	Derek White	c	Derek Cousins
b	Derek Wyatt	d	Derek Cousines

7.15 Who was the first prop to win 50 caps against International Board countries?

a	Andy Carmichael	c	Dandy Carmichael
b	Sandy Carmichael	d	Bandy Carmichael

7.16 Who were the only team to beat Scotland under Jim Aitken?

a	England	c	New Zealand
b	Ireland	d	Romania

7.17 Name the only country unbeaten in the 1974 World Cup?

a	West Germany	c	Italy
b	Holland	d	Scotland

7.18 Name a Scottish club which never had a player capped at full international level?

a	Berwick Rangers	c	Stirling Albion
b	Stenhousemuir	d	All of these

7.19 Name the Dutch refugee who won 17 rugby caps for Scotland?

a	Franz Nine Bos	c	Franz Itchy Bos
b	Franz Two Bos	d	Franz Ten Bos

7.20 Which country has reached all of the World Cup Finals?

a	Uraguay	c	West Germany
b	Brazil	d	Italy

7.21 An Olympic weightlifting silver medallist played a part in *Goldfinger*. What was his character's name?

a	Jaws	c	Oddjob
b	Oddfinger	d	Bobajob

7.22 And his real name?

a	Harold Sakata	c	Harold Potato
b	Humphrey Sakata	d	Humphrey Potato

7.23 Who is the only man to have beaten Jim Watt in Scotland?

a	Ken Buchanan	c	Rocky Marciano
b	Mario D'Agata	d	Prince Rodney

7.24 Who won the Italian Grand Prix in 2001?

a	Juan Pablo Montoya	c	Rubens Barrichello
b	Michael Schumacher	d	Ralf Schumacher

7.25 Who recorded the Ben E. King hit 'Stand By Me' in 1964?

a	Rueben Carter	c	Joe Frazier
b	Muhammed Ali	d	Ernie Shavers

7.26 Who won the President's Cup in Tashkent in 2001?

a	Kafelnikov	c	Meligeni
b	Safin	d	Varek

7.27 In which sport is the Strathcona Cup played?

a	Ice hockey	c	Shinty
b	Curling	d	Hockey

7.28 Where was the Scottish National run up to 1966?

a	Bogside	c	Musselburgh
b	Ayr	d	Selkirk

7.29 How many players in a hockey team?

a	11	c	10
b	12	d	9

7.30 How long is each half in a hockey match?

a	45 minutes	c	40 minutes
b	50 minutes	d	35 minutes

7.31 Two countries lay claim to the origin of curling. Scotland is one. Name the other.

a	Canada	c	USA
b	Holland	d	Germany

7.32 What is curling's World Championship trophy called?

a	Golden Broom	c	Diamond Broom
b	Bronze Broom	d	Silver Broom

7.33 In curling, over what distance is the stone thrown?

a	40 yards	c	45 yards
b	35 yards	d	50 yards

7.34 In curling, what is the playing surface called?

a	The flat bit	c	The ice
b	The rink	d	The bonspeil

7.35 In darts, what is the height from the floor to the centre of the bull?

a	5ft 6in	c	5ft 10in
b	5ft 8in	d	5ft 4in

7.36 Which was the last course to stage two successive British Opens?

a	St Andrews	c	Troon
b	Royal Birkdale	d	Carnoustie

7.37 On which course can the 'Postage Stamp' be found?

a	St Andrews	c	Troon
b	Royal Birkdale	d	Carnoustie

7.38 Who is the patron saint of ice-skating?

a	St Brigid	c	St Lydwina of Schiedam
b	St Frigid	d	St Francis

7.39 What sport were the Toucan Terribles involved in?

a	Marbles	c	American Football
b	Rugby League	d	Guinness drinking

7.40 How many times has a Scot won a title at Wimbledon?

a	Once	c	Twice
b	Never	d	Five times

7.41 Who won the Marine Hanest Shinty final in 2001?

a	The West	c	The East
b	The South	d	The North

7.42 Which golfer was known as the Silvery Scot?

a	Colin Montgomery	c	Peter Thomson
b	Tommy Armour	d	Peter Allis

7.43 What is the longest course in the British Open rota?

a	St Andrews Old Course	c	Troon
b	Carnoustie	d	Lytham St Annes

7.44 Which popular singer of the '50s and '60s pitched for the Houston Buffaloes?

a	Frankie Laine	c	Buddy Holly
b	Frank Sinatra	d	Jim Reeves

7.45 What is the name of North America's principal ice-hockey competition?

a	The Oliver Cup	c	The Laurel Cup
b	The Stanley Cup	d	The Hardy Cup

7.46 What trophy do Scotland and England contest at Rugby Union?

a	The Madras Cup	c	The Delhi Cup
b	The Calcutta Cup	d	The Darjeeling Cup

7.47 What sport contests for the Bowring Bowl?

a	Snooker	c	Rugby Union
b	Rugby League	d	Powerboat Racing

7.48 Who won the Cameron Corbett Vase in 2001?

a	Bault	c	MacRae
b	Bryson	d	Cameron

7.49 What was Ian McLaughlan's nickname?

a	The Mouse	c	King Rat
b	Mighty Mouse	d	Marvelmouse

7.50 Which rugby club did he play for?

a	Boroughmuir	c	Heriots
b	Jordanhill	d	Kelso

'I'd sooner starve.'
Julia Roberts,
June 1994, when asked if
she'd like some haggis

'Cheese – milk's leap
toward immortality.'
Clifton Fadiman,
of whom the Duke of
Edinburgh once said,
'Who?'

8

Glaswegians and Food

Glaswegians love food in all its multifarious guises. When it was announced that we were to be getting refugees from the ethnic Albanian population of Kosovo, not to mention people fleeing the Taliban, the first question on Glasgwegian lips was, 'What will their chips be like?' Just joking. There will, of course, be an Albanian and an Afghani restaurant along some time soon, if there isn't one already. Alba would be a good name for the former, as the word means Scotland in the old tongue, and a lot of Glasgow's restaurants and shops are now offering things like cranachan and rumbledethumps.

Ronnie Clydesdale started the Ubiquitous Chip in 1977 on the simple, but at that time untried, premise that

Glasgow people would eat and enjoy home-grown produce. Ronnie asserts that Scotland has the finest cuisine and raw materials to be had anywhere, as the success of his green and leafy enclave in the West End has proved. It was an idea whose time had come, and the days when it was a choice of chips or expensive French cuisine requiring a Pools win to finance it were over.

We now have restaurants from every corner of the world, especially Asia. Glasgow is the curry capital of the world, though nobody quite knows why. It may be the fact that curry is delicious and relatively inexpensive, or it may be the Glaswegian penchant for the new, not to mention the nippy, or it may just be typically Glaswegian luck. The Pakistanis, Indians, Chinese, Thais and others came here, found friendly faces and foodie niches, and stayed. Now their children and grandchildren say, 'Gonny geez a hudgie, Grandpa?' just like everybody else, and order hairst bree, howtowdie and Cullen skink in our increasingly ethnic Scottish and Glaswegian restaurants.

'Bring back Scottish names!' is the cry. It is more fun eating 'hairst bree' than 'lamb broth' and 'howtowdie' sounds and tastes better than 'boiled chicken' does it not? You'll find more than several Scottish words in the next list of questions. Even if you don't know the answers, learn them. They'll come in handy at a restaurant near you sometime soon. And have you ever seen a restaurant in Glasgow which sells deep-fried Mars bars? If you have, keep it quiet.

8.1 What number in Dumbarton Road is Two Fat Ladies?

a	77	c	66
b	88	d	99

8.2 Where is the Ubiquitous Chip?

a	Under the fish	c	Under the other chips
b	Ashton Lane	d	On a Glaswegian shoulder

8.3 What can't you get at the Ubiquitous Chip?

a	Chips	c	Mashed potatoes
b	Boiled potatoes	d	Stoved potatoes

8.4 What is hairst bree?

a	Lamb broth	c	Lamb stew
b	Hare soup	d	Hare stew

8.5 What is hotch-potch?

a	Another name for stovies	c	Another name for lamb stew
b	Another name for hairst bree	d	Another name for hare stew

8.6 What is a bap?

| a | An American clout on the ear | c | A crusty loaf |
| b | A yeasted roll | d | A dance |

8.7 What is the principal filling of an Adelaide sandwich?

| a | Veal and ham | c | Tongue and veal |
| b | Chicken and veal | d | Chicken and ham |

8.8 What else could you use instead of chicken?

| a | Sardines | c | Sild |
| b | Anchovies | d | Tuna |

8.9 What are the main ingredients (by weight) of a Dundee cake?

| a | Butter and sugar | c | Currants and raisins |
| b | Flour and milk | d | Cherries and brandy |

8.10 What is redware?

| a | A bull attractant | c | Coloured ceramic |
| b | Seaweed | d | A kind of grass |

8.11 What is sloke?

a	A seaweed	c	A slow cooking method
b	A kind of grass	d	A fuel

8.12 What is a collop?

a	A fast pace for a horse	c	An English clout on the ear
b	A kind of fish	d	A thin slice of meat

8.13 What is cranachan?

a	Gaelic for snotters	c	A seaweed
b	A cream crowdie	d	A kind of grass

8.14 What are petticoat tails?

a	Wee dangly things under a petticoat	c	Square bits of shortbread
b	Triangular bits of shortbread	d	Fingers of shortbread

8.15 What is cock-a-leekie?

a	A urinary problem	c	A kind of chicken soup
b	Scotch broth	d	Mutton stew

8.16 What are crullas?

| a | People called De Ville | c | Small cakes |
| b | Sheep | d | Shearing tongs |

8.17 What are butteries?

| a | Dundee rolls | c | Aberdeen rolls |
| b | Lewis rolls | d | Edinburgh rolls |

8.18 What are melting moments?

| a | Before you propose marriage | c | Scones |
| b | Biscuits | d | That bit just before your mum clouts you |

8.19 What is the principal ingredient (by weight) of Dundee marmalade?

| a | Lemons | c | Sugar |
| b | Water | d | Oranges |

8.20 What is ham and haddies?

| a | Motherwell strikers | c | Two bad actors |
| b | Smoked ham and poached fish | d | A kind of cart |

8.21 What is black bun?

a	Your grannie's hairdo	c	Horse droppings
b	Fruit cake	d	A dark rabbit

8.22 What is Broonie?

a	Burnt sugar	c	Treacle
b	Gingerbread	d	Cinnamon

8.23 What is het pint?

a	A heated mixture of beer and whisky	c	A tennis score
b	A disputed matter	d	A warmed brandy

8.24 What is the main ingredient of howtowdie?

a	Ham	c	Mutton
b	Beef	d	Chicken

8.25 What is the principal ingredient of Newhaven cream?

a	Milk	c	Eggs
b	Breadcrumbs	d	Fish

8.26 What is a Selkirk bannock?

a	Fruit loaf	c	A floured scone
b	A fruit scone	d	A treacle scone

8.27 What is the principal ingredient of skirlie?

a	Bagpipes	c	Onion
b	Oatmeal	d	Suet

8.28 What is the principal ingredient of Scotch woodcock?

a	Woodcock	c	Anchovies
b	Egg yolks	d	Cream

8.29 Is Caledonian cream . . . ?

a	A whisky	c	A dessert
b	A starter	d	A main course

8.30 What spirit is used in making Atholl brose?

a	Whisky	c	Rum
b	Brandy	d	Gin

8.31 What is a diet loaf?

| a | Something called Nimble | c | A low-calorie bread |
| b | A sponge cake | d | Something prisoners eat |

8.32 What are speldings?

| a | People who can't spell | c | Small salmon |
| b | Small cod | d | Small trout |

8.33 What do the English call dropped scones?

| a | Careless | c | Muffins |
| b | Pancakes | d | Oatcakes |

8.34 What is cullen skink?

| a | Thick fish soup | c | A kind of dried fish |
| b | Thin fish soup | d | A kind of chicken stew |

8.35 What is a bubbly-jock?

| a | A crying Scotsman | c | A grouse |
| b | A turkey | d | A wood pigeon |

8.36 What is the main ingredient of Tweed kettle?

a	Rabbit	c	Hare
b	Salmon	d	Turkey

8.37 Another word for spurtle is ... ?

a	Theevil	c	Stirrie
b	Spoonie	d	Stoogie

8.38 What is the Gaelic brochan in English?

a	Broken	c	A small house
b	A burying cist	d	Porridge

8.39 Where would you find mashlam scones?

a	Under a bus	c	Mull
b	Iona	d	Near a distillery

8.40 What is mashlam?

a	Wheat	c	Corn
b	Barley	d	A mixture of grains

8.41 Who would eat aiger brose?

| a | Aigerians | c | Beggars |
| b | Beekeepers | d | Children |

8.42 What is aiger?

| a | A mixture of grains | c | Barley |
| b | Oats | d | Corn |

8.43 What is rumbledethumps?

| a | A good doing in Glasgow | c | A good doing in Aberdeen |
| b | Potatoes and cabbage | d | Potatoes and turnip |

8.44 What is clapshot?

| a | What you do at clay pigeon shoots | c | What you do at Motherwell games |
| b | Potatoes and turnip | d | Potatoes and cabbage |

8.45 How do you cook colcannon?

| a | In the oven | c | Spit-roast it |
| b | Boil it | d | Fry it |

8.46 What kind of pudding is an urney?

a	Fruit	c	Sponge
b	Ice cream	d	Chocolate

8.47 What is a hodgil?

a	A thing for keeping rabbits	c	An oatmeal dumpling
b	A lentil bake	d	A scallop

8.48 What is hoobjooblie?

a	A mixture of fruit juice and milk	c	Fruit juice and honey
b	Honey and milk	d	A made-up word

8.49 Which Glasgow restaurant is named after a Russian recluse?

a	Lermentov's	c	Kruschev's
b	Oblomov's	d	Bulganin's

8.50 What is a babbity bowster?

a	A game played with razors	c	A Glasgow hotel/restaurant/pub
b	A game played by women	d	A game played with cudgels

9

'Architecture . . . history
written in stone.'
  Charles Rennie Mackintosh

'Geography is people.'
  Willie MacIlvanney

'History is bunk.'
  Henry Ford

Architecture, Geography and a Bit More History

Everybody who visited Glasgow in the 17th and 18th centuries had something nice to say about it. They liked the broad streets and the stone rather than brick–built houses – houses made to last. It's a shame that they, by and large, didn't. We have never hesitated to get rid of things when we decide that we don't want them anymore and the Victorians, with their overweening self-confidence and faith in the future, were no exception, razing whole areas and building anew. And they built well, buildings made to last. And most of them have.

Despite the town-planning decision to relocate our slums outside the city, and despite the wholesale demolition of entire streets and areas that were much better than their replacements – just overcrowded and badly maintained – and despite the high-rise and motorway madness of the '60s and '70s, a lot of Victorian Glasgow remains in remark-ably well-preserved condition. It is solid, part of the Glaswegian mind-set. It was there when we were born, and it will be there when our children's children are born, because it is beautiful. Lord Esher says in his *Conservation of Glasgow* in 1971, 'Glasgow is now the finest surviving example of a great Victorian city.' Can you imagine someone wanting to knock down the Kelvingrove Museum and Art Gallery? There would be hundreds of thousands of people placing their bodies between it and destruction. It is ours, much like the People's Palace, part of our lives, part of our history. Anyone who wishes to be a

Who Wants to be a Glaswegian?

Glaswegian should remember this. We've made mistakes, sure, but some things will remain forever.

We didn't have the chance to do that Edinburgh thing – 'Great castle, let's build a row of really ugly shops opposite it and call it Princes Street' – because we don't have a castle, hurray! We do have a rotating tower and a thing that looks like the state animal of Texas opposite each other on the banks of the Clyde, and we do have the work of two world-class architects, Mackintosh and Thomson, all around us.

So wander the streets, up Sauchie and down Buchie, etc. Lift your head; look up. Glasgow is a great city to look up in.

9.1 Where is Dissy Corner?

a	Union Street and Argyle Street	c	London Road
b	Copland Road	d	Jamaica Street and Argyle Street

9.2 Where is St George's Church?

a	George Square	c	Nelson Mandela Place
b	Victoria Road	d	St George's Cross

9.3 When was it built?

a	1921	c	1812
b	1807	d	1907

9.4 Who designed it?

a	David Stark	c	William Stark
b	John Streaker	d	David Streaker

9.5 Who is on the plinth in the middle of George Square?

a	Robert Burns	c	Sir Walter Scott
b	Pat Lally	d	Sir Robert Peel

9.6 Why is the figure facing South?

a	He asked for this in his will	c	He's expecting George III
b	It isn't	d	An accident

9.7 Who was his favourite architect?

a	David Stark	c	William Stark
b	John Naked	d	David Naked

9.8 What street is Glasgow Royal Infirmary in?

a	Keep Street	c	High Street
b	East Street	d	Castle Street

9.9 When did it open?

a	1794	c	1798
b	1894	d	1898

9.10 Who pioneered germ-killing techniques there?

a	Auntie Septic	c	David Lister
b	Joseph Lister	d	John Lister

9.11 Where is Glasgow Cathedral?

a	High Street	c	Fort Street
b	Castle Street	d	Stronghold Lane

9.12 In which century was the present structure built?

a	14th	c	13th
b	12th	d	11th

9.13 St Mungo's Tomb is there. When did he die?

a	603 AD	c	803 AD
b	703 AD	d	503 AD

9.14 Where is the only Zen garden in the UK?

a	Inside your head	c	St Mungo's Museum
b	The City Chambers	d	The Burrell

9.15 Where is Baird's Hall?

a	Bath Street	c	Sauchiehall Street
b	Renfrew Street	d	St Vincent Street

9.16 What was it originally?

a	The Beresford Hotel	c	The Blythswood Hotel
b	The Charing Cross Hotel	d	The Stakis Hotel

9.17 What architectural style is it?

a	Art Nouveau	c	Rococo
b	Arty Farty	d	Art Deco

9.18 What is it now?

a	A youth hostel	c	Student accommodation
b	A dosshouse	d	A backpacker's stop

9.19 Where is Glasgow School of Art?

a	Renfield Street	c	Renfrew Road
b	Renfrew Street	d	Renfield Lane

9.20 Where did Charles Rennie Mackintosh die?

a	Glasgow	c	London
b	South of France	d	Edinburgh

9.21 Of what?

| a | A heart attack | c | Cancer |
| b | Neglect | d | A stroke |

9.22 What architectural style is the Glasgow School of Art?

| a | Art Deco | c | Chocolate Box |
| b | Wedding Cake | d | Art Nouveau |

9.23 Where is the Mitchell Library?

| a | Berkley Street | c | Barclay Street |
| b | Berkeley Street | d | Berkley Square |

9.24 Who founded it?

| a | Stephen Mitchell | c | Charles Mitchell |
| b | The Mitchellin Man | d | John Mitchell |

9.25 Who laid the foundation stone?

| a | The Earl of Roseberry | c | W. B. Whitie |
| b | Andrew Carnegie | d | W. B. Blackie |

9.26   Where is the Pearce Institute?

| a | Eglinton Toll | c | Govan Cross |
| b | The Round Toll | d | Glasgow Cross |

9.27   What sits on top of it?

| a | A crane | c | A sailing ship |
| b | A steamship | d | A cross |

9.28   Who financed it?

| a | Sir Thomas Pearce | c | Sir David Pearce |
| b | Sir William Pearce | d | Sir John Pearce |

9.29   Which shipyard was he chairman of?

| a | Harland and Woolf | c | William Denny |
| b | Fairfields | d | Lithgows |

9.30   If you were his statue, looking round present-day Govan, would you . . . ?

| a | Despair | c | Laugh |
| b | Cheer | d | Fall on your knees and give thanks |

9.31 Who designed Charing Cross Mansions?

a	Sir J. J. Burnet	c	A madman
b	Charles Rennie Mackintosh	d	Sir Basil Spence

9.32 Where was the first place in Glasgow to be lit by gas?

a	A grocer's in the Trongate	c	George Square
b	An ironmonger's in the Trongate	d	Blythswood Square

9.33 Where is the oldest pub in Glasgow?

a	London Road	c	Shettleston Road
b	Trongate	d	Saltmarket

9.34 When was it built?

a	1717	c	1517
b	1617	d	1417

9.35 Where did Irn Bru start?

a	Ruchill	c	Ibrox
b	Saltmarket	d	Parkhead

9.36 From where was the author of *Ye Mariners of England*?

a	Glasgow	c	London
b	Edinburgh	d	York

9.37 From where does Glasgow's water supply come?

a	Loch Long	c	Loch Katrine
b	Loch Lomond	d	Loch Ness

9.38 Where was the first Glasgow Post Office?

a	Trongate	c	High Street
b	Saltmarket	d	Duke Street

9.39 Where were Glasgow's first high-rise flats built?

a	Red Road	c	Cardonald
b	Gorbals	d	Parkhead

9.40 When?

a	1950	c	1960
b	1955	d	1945

9.41 Where did Glasgow's first public hangings take place?

a	Glasgow Cross	c	George Square
b	Glasgow Green	d	Cathedral Square

9.42 Where is Lord Kelvin buried?

a	Westminster Abbey	c	The Ramshorn
b	The Necropolis	d	Glasgow Cathedral

9.43 George Burns, founder of Cunard, was born where?

a	Burns Street	c	Robert Street
b	George Street	d	Poets Place

9.44 Ibrox comes from the Gaelic for . . . ?

a	Place of the Fox	c	Place of the Badger
b	Place of the Blue Noses	d	Place of the Numpties

9.45 Gorbals means . . . ?

a	Beautiful Town	c	God's Garden
b	Pretty Place	d	South Land

9.46 Garngad means . . . ?

a	Beautiful Town	c	God's Garden
b	Pretty Place	d	South Land

9.47 Was God green-fingered that day?

a	No	c	No
b	No	d	No

9.48 What is Eggie Toll officially called?

a	St Peter's Cross	c	St Andrew's Cross
b	St John's Cross	d	St Patrick's Cross

9.49 Where was the airship *R34* built?

a	Beardmore's	c	Fairfields
b	Findlay's	d	Harland and Woolf

9.50 Who designed the Trades House in Glassford Street?

a	Peter Adam	c	Robert Adam
b	The Addams Family	d	William Adam

10

The Clyde, Ships and Socialism

> 'The red will be worn, my lads, and Scotland will march again noo great John Maclean has come hame tae the Clyde.'
>
> Hamish Henderson, *The John Maclean March*, 1948

'The Clyde made Glasgow and Glasgow made the Clyde' is a saying so well used that it doesn't really need quotation marks round it. But it is no longer true. When shipbuilding went away to deeper channels and cheaper labour, and most of the West of Scotland poured sewage and industrial waste into it, the Clyde suffered badly. 'The hammers' ding-dong', isn't the song of the Clyde any more, nor will it be in the foreseeable future, but that doesn't mean that the river is dead.

Legislation has meant cleaner water and the salmon are back. Glaswegian workers used to have a clause in their contracts which stated that they could not be paid more than the equivalent of one day's wages in salmon. Tales are told of wee boys walking across the river

on the backs of the salmon, so plentiful were they. Maybe that will happen again. Don't hold your breath, though, but there will be a lot more fishermen on the river and fishermen have to eat, drink and have somewhere to stay.

In a post-industrial Glasgow, what can we sell? The Clyde, of course. We want tall-ships museums, museums of steamers, industrial museums that show how our fathers and grandfathers sweated and gave of their blood to feed their families. Shipbuilding, particularly in the early days, was a horrendous job. It killed people in their thousands. Reading the casualty lists of just one year is like reading about the first day of the Somme.

As well as building ships, the Clyde built men. There is a lot of romantic nonsense talked about shipbuilding and the yards, but the conditions and the attitude of the owners built solidarity and socialism into entire communities. The lore and the skills may be lost, but the feelings persist. Fairness is important to Glaswegians and injustice is as hotly resisted now as it was then. Why not a museum of socialism, reconstructions of the return of John Maclean, the UCS sit-inners in conference, historic strike votes?

You may well smile, but we need to use the river and we need to use the people. The Greater Glasgow Tourist Board will welcome ideas. In the meantime, how is your knowledge of shipbuilding's history?

10.1 What, according to the song, is 'The Song of the Clyde'?

| a | 'That's not fair' | c | 'Giddy up a ding-dong' |
| b | 'The hammers' ding-dong' | d | 'Equal pay for equal work' |

10.2 Where does the Clyde rise?

| a | Near Moffat | c | Near Biggar |
| b | Near Motherwell | d | Near Peebles |

10.3 How many shipbuilding yards were there in Glasgow in 1880?

| a | Around 70 | c | Around 100 |
| b | Around 50 | d | Around 150 |

10.4 Which is the world's oldest shipbuilding organisation?

| a | Scott's of Greenock | c | Harland and Woolf |
| b | Fairfields | d | John Wood of Port Glasgow |

10.5 What was the first iron ship called?

| a | *Old Ironsides* | c | *Spock* |
| b | *Vulcan* | d | *Wotan* |

10.6 Where was she built?

| a | Faskine | c | Port Glasgow |
| b | Erskine | d | Greenock |

10.7 What was the first iron ship to sail on the Clyde named?

| a | *The Faerie Queene* | c | *The Marion* |
| b | *The Fairy Queen* | d | *The Maid Marion* |

10.8 Powered by . . . ?

| a | Steam | c | Oars |
| b | Sail | d | Clockwork |

10.9 When did Tod and MacGregor set up the first yard exclusively to build iron ships?

| a | 1834 | c | 1824 |
| b | 1844 | d | 1854 |

10.10 When did the Boilermakers Society start?

| a | 1834 | c | 1824 |
| b | 1842 | d | 1854 |

10.11 Who were the best paid tradesmen on the Clyde in the 1920s?

a	Welders	c	Electricians
b	Riveters	d	Joiners

10.12 What is the oldest steel trade?

a	Plater	c	Shipwright
b	Riveter	d	Loftsmen

10.13 At the launch of the *QE2*, what was Queen Elizabeth given?

a	A large whisky	c	The Freedom of Glasgow
b	A speedboat	d	The *QE2*

10.14 What happened at the launch of the *Daphne* in 1883?

a	She exploded	c	She capsized
b	She rolled over in the stocks	d	She stuck in the opposite bank

10.15 How many men and boys were killed?

a	124	c	100
b	70	d	101

10.16 Who built the *Empress of Japan*?

a	Fairfields	c	John Brown's
b	Harland and Woolf	d	Tod and MacGregor

10.17 What was she renamed in 1942?

a	*Empress of Britain*	c	*Empress of Scotland*
b	*Empress of England*	d	*Empress of Australia*

10.18 Who built the paddle ferry *Mary Queen of Scots*?

a	Denny of Dumbarton	c	John Brown's
b	Tod and MacGregor	d	Steffens

10.19 Where did she ply?

a	The Clyde	c	The Ganges
b	The Forth	d	Lake Erie

10.20 Name another in her class.

a	*Robert the Bruce*	c	*Robert Burns*
b	*Bonny Prince Charlie*	d	*Prince Charles*

10.21 Who built the world's first roll-on roll-off ferry?

a	Denny of Dumbarton	c	John Brown's
b	Tod and MacGregor	d	Harland and Woolf

10.22 Who built *Redgauntlet*?

a	Denny of Dumbarton	c	John Brown's
b	Tod and MacGregor	d	Barclay Curle

10.23 Who built *Intrepid*, which sailed with the Falklands Task Force?

a	Denny of Dumbarton	c	John Brown's
b	Barclay Curle	d	Steffens

10.24 What was the *QE2*'s yard number?

a	534	c	531
b	736	d	731

10.25 When was she launched?

a	1965	c	1967
b	1966	d	1968

10.26 What was Yarrow's first name?

a	John	c	David
b	Robert	d	Alfred

10.27 And Messrs Barclay and Curle were both called . . . ?

a	John	c	David
b	Robert	d	Alfred

10.28 Who built the *Waverley*?

a	Denny of Dumbarton	c	John Brown's
b	A. & J. Inglis	d	Stephen's

10.29 When?

a	1947	c	1946
b	1948	d	1949

10.30 What does 'steamboats' mean in Glasgow?

a	Clyde-built shipping	c	Puffers
b	Drunk	d	A kind of reefer

10.31 What is Fairfield's now called?

a	Kvaerner Govan Ltd	c	Govan Shipbuilders
b	UCS	d	Stephen's

10.32 What was the 534?

a	*Queen Mary*	c	*Queen Elizabeth*
b	*Empress of India*	d	*QE2*

10.33 Where did the *Queen Elizabeth* end her days?

a	Los Angeles	c	Hong Kong
b	Broken up	d	The Thames

10.34 What percentage of Britain's iron tonnage did the Clyde produce from 1851–70?

a	15 per cent	c	25 per cent
b	80 per cent	d	50 per cent

10.35 How long was the working week for skilled trades in 1913?

a	60 hours	c	50 hours
b	54 hours	d	44 hours

10.36 Before the War of Independence in America, where were most of the Clyde's ships built?

a	The Clyde	c	Humberside
b	America	d	Tyneside

10.37 What was the colour of an Anchor Line funnel?

a	Red	c	Yellow
b	Black	d	Green

10.38 And the hull?

a	Black, red waterline	c	Blue, red waterline
b	Red, black waterline	d	Black, green waterline

10.39 What colour was a Blue Funnel Line's funnel?

a	Blue, red top	c	Blue, yellow top
b	Red, blue top	d	Blue, black top

10.40 And the hull?

a	Red, black waterline	c	Blue, red waterline
b	Black, red waterline	d	Black, green waterline

10.41 What was the name of the first vessel commissioned for Cunard's trans-Atlantic service?

a	*Columbia*	c	*Caledonia*
b	*Britannia*	d	*Acadia*

10.42 Who was her most illustrious passenger?

a	Oscar Wilde	c	Charles Darwin
b	Charles Dickens	d	Queen Victoria

10.43 Who, in 'The John Maclean March', were marching from Clydebank?

a	The jiners and hauders-on	c	The jiners and platers
b	The riveters	d	The welders

10.44 When did work on the 534 stop?

a	1931	c	1934
b	1933	d	1932

10.45 When did it restart?

a	1935	c	1934
b	1936	d	1933

10.46 How many of John Brown's workforce were laid off when work stopped on the 534?

a	Over 1000	c	Over 500
b	Over 3000	d	Over 2000

10.47 In 1931 how many times a week had you to sign on the dole?

a	Three	c	One
b	Two	d	Not at all

10.48 Where were the toilets that the shipbuilders used on board?

a	On the after deck	c	In the double bottom
b	On the poop deck	d	There were none

10.49 What were riveters called?

a	The Green Gang	c	The Navy Gang
b	The Black Gang	d	The Red Gang

10.50 How were riveters paid?

a	Per rivet	c	Basic wage
b	Basic wage and bonus	d	Basic wage and overtime

THE ANSWERS

History

1.1	
b	The Clyde
1.2	
c	Mungo
1.3	
a	Fife
1.4	
b	A heap of Ice Age rubble
1.5	
d	A Salmon
1.6	
d	All of these
1.7	
b	Levitate
1.8	
b	Cistercians
1.9	
c	July
1.10	
c	A gangrenous disease
1.11	
b	1603
1.12	
a	Panama
1.13	
a	1707
1.14	
c	Rum
1.15	
c	*QE2*

1.16	
b	*Comet*
1.17	
d	Wishful thinking
1.18	
d	1990
1.19	
ALL	All are correct
1.20	
c	Royal Scottish National Orchestra
1.21	
d	Dali
1.22	
a	Tom Honeyman
1.23	
b	1952 — d	Yonks ago
1.24	
d	£8200
1.25	
b	Duncan MacRae
1.26	
a	*Whisky Galore*
1.27	
c	*Geordie*
1.28	
a	*Tunes of Glory*
1.29	
d	Benny Lynch
1.30	
b	Gorbals

1.31

a	33

1.32

c	The Citizen's Theatre

1.33

a	A two-legged horse

1.34

a	El Fideldo

1.35

b	Her folks wanted a wee boy horse

1.36

b	Lobey Dosser

1.37

b	Rank Bajin

1.38

b	1867

1.39

a	1872

1.40

b	Partick

1.41

d	11

1.42

a	0–0

1.43

b	The Spiders

1.44

d	Glasgow's first public baths

1.45

b	Pat Lally

1.46

b	*Lazarus Only Done It Once*

1.47

d	Only the Labour Party knows

1.48

b	The Suspension Bridge

1.49

a	None

1.50

b	Lord Wellington

1.51

a	It's funny

1.52

c	Goths

1.53

d	Skateboarders

1.54

b	Divans

1.55

b	Dive-on

1.56

c	Will Fyffe

1.57

c	Jim Kelman

1.58

b	*The Great Northern Welly Boot Show*

1.59

b	*Me Wi' a Bad Leg Tae*

1.60

a	1842

Attitude, Language and the Patter

2.1

| d | A howling eejit |

2.2

| b | Who's askin? |

2.3

| d | Flight |

2.4

| c | Celtic superstar Henrik Larsson |

2.5

| b | Dae that |

2.6

| d | Jist gonny no |

2.7

| b | Yer Maw |

2.8

| c | Hamish Imlach |

2.9

| c | Matt McGinn |

2.10

| d | Double Time |

2.11

| a | In France |

2.12

| a | Eastwood Cemetery |

2.13

| c | Duncan Macrae |

2.14

| b | A slow dance |

2.15

| a | Battering lumps out of them |

2.16

| b | A small gift |

2.17

| d | A Transcard |

2.18

| b | A black cab |

2.19

| c | Spectacles |

2.20

| a | A crumbly confection |

2.21

| b | Small fish |

2.22

| a | Police cars |

2.23

| c | A forced marriage |

2.24

| a | Nasal mucilage |

2.25

| b | Embarrassment |

2.26

| b | Anyone who can't answer this |

2.27

| b | Fingers |

2.28

| b | Sydney Devine |

2.29

| b | Legal Aid |

2.30

| b | Partick Thistle |

2.31

c	A swindler

2.32

b	A male homosexual

2.33

a	A bitter lemming

2.34

b	Alex Glasgow

2.35

c	A lift

2.36

d	Skitterywinter

2.37

d	Snookered

2.38

c	He's awa' noo

2.39

c	CND supporters

2.40

b	Oot o' the East

2.41

a	Orange

2.42

a	Your mother's maternal parent

2.43

a	The Humble one

2.44

a	The Pavilion

2.45

b	Queen's Park

2.46

b	A lamplighter

2.47

b	A tiled common entrance

2.48

a	Celtic Football Club

2.49

b	Rangers Football Club

2.50

c	An appeal to desist

Theatre and Music Hall

3.1
c	Renfield Street

3.2
d	Bath Street

3.3
c	Sauchiehall Street

3.4
b	The Trongate

3.5
c	Under the Heilanman's Umbrella

3.6
b	Hope Street

3.7
c	A library

3.8
b	An arty space on the South Side

3.9
a	A theatre in the Gorbals

3.10
b	Tramway

3.11
c	The Tron

3.12
b	The Arches

3.13
c	The Old Athenaeum

3.14
c	15,000

3.15
a	*Metropolis*

3.16
c	In Ingram Street

3.17
ALL	All are correct

3.18
b	At the corner of Waterloo Street

3.19
a	1897

3.20
b	Vesta Tilley

3.21
c	Billy Bennett

3.22
c	The colour of the Empire's upholstery

3.23
d	Gene Autry

3.24
a	1963

3.25
a	1910

3.26
a	1969

3.27
a	Cilla Black

3.28
b	Trongate

3.29
b	Albert E. Pickard

3.30
b	The Panopticon

3.31

b	1905

3.32

a	A lion

3.33

b	Frank Matcham

3.34

a	The Bodie Riot

3.35

b	Jimmy Logan

3.36

c	Footing the bill

3.37

a	Tommy Lorne

3.38

b	The coos

3.39

c	Shot himself

3.40

b	It has a sliding roof

3.41

a	Duncan Macrae and Albert Finney

3.42

c	Took pickaxes to the stage

3.43

a	38 weeks

3.44

b	Pierce Brosnan

3.45

d	Black

3.46

b	Buy freedom

3.47

d	1963

3.48

c	*Hamlet*

3.49

c	On the front page

3.50

a	Allen Wright

The Dancin'

4.1

a	12

4.2

d	5

4.3

d	All of these

4.4

a	1923

4.5

a	Mills and Siele

4.6

a	She was related to John Mills

4.7

a	She manipulated Muffin the Mule

4.8

b	'Please Charleston Quietly'

4.9

c	Beryl Evetts

4.10

b	The men danced with their caps on

4.11

a	1928

4.12

b	1000

4.13

b	Clabber dancing

4.14

a	Select dancing

4.15

d	10,000

4.16

b	Until 1957

4.17

c	'The Emperor's Tango'

4.18

a	1938

4.19

a	A supermarket

4.20

d	All of these

4.21

b	1000

4.22

d	You put your right hand in

4.23

d	99

4.24

a	101

4.25

b	1934

4.26

b	Mrs Margaret McIver

4.27

b	The Gaybirds

4.28

a	The fountain

4.29

d	1990

4.30

b	He died

4.31

b	Barrowland

4.32

b	Their neon sign

4.33

c	A gas mask

4.34

d	The Lord's Day Observance Society

4.35

a	Jitterbug Alley

4.36

c	A lumber

4.37

a	*Ebbtide*

4.38

a	Flash

4.39

b	The Starlight Formation

4.40

c	Alan Freed

4.41

b	Barrowland

4.42

b	Tiffany's

4.43

c	A casino

4.44

a	Bible John

4.45

b	Barrowland

4.46

b	1964

4.47

c	Bill and Bobby

4.48

b	Donnie and Gaynor

4.49

a	Ashfield

4.50

c	1973

Art, Culture and That

5.1

| c | A Radox foot bath bucks up your feet |

5.2

| a | 1962 |

5.3

| d | *Madame Butterfly* |

5.4

| a | Cio Cio San |

5.5

| b | Puccini |

5.6

| a | Sir Alexander Gibson |

5.7

| b | Theatre Royal |

5.8

| a | The King's |

5.9

| a | Albert Herring |

5.10

| a | Dalziel High, Motherwell |

5.11

| d | *The Bartered Bride* |

5.12

| c | Smetana |

5.12

| a | The Glasgow Grand Opera Society |

5.14

| c | Mozart |

5.15

| a | A soprano |

5.16

| a | There isn't one, ha ha |

5.17

| c | Springburn |

5.18

| d | Dunoon |

5.19

| d | Seven shillings and sixpence |

5.20

| b | A lute |

5.21

| d | 1906 |

5.22

| a | 1969 |

5.23

| b | King's |

5.24

| b | *The Trojans* |

5.25

| c | Berlioz |

5.26

| a | Peter Darrell |

5.27

| b | Hazel Merry |

5.28

| b | 1959 |

5.29

| a | Swarowsky |

5.30

| a | 1962 |

5.31

a	1841

5.32

a	Neeme Jarvi

5.33

c	Dvořák

5.34

b	Johann Strauss II

5.35

a	Ludwig van Beethoven

5.36

a	1786

5.37

b	Joseph

5.38

b	George Frideric

5.39

a	Georges

5.40

c	*Carmen*

5.41

b	The Merchants' Hall

5.42

c	*Victory*

5.43

d	Cologne Cathedral

5.44

b	Rodin

5.45

c	Van Gogh

5.46

d	The Burrell

5.47

c	Peter Howson

5.48

b	*The Herald*

5.49

a	1996

5.50

b	Eduard Bersudsky

Football

6.1
c	The Teddy Bears

6.2
a	The Tim Malloys

6.3
d	The Bully Wee

6.4
c	The Jags

6.5
b	Rangers

6.6
a	Celtic

6.7
d	Motherwell

6.8
d	Motherwell

6.9
c	Hearts

6.10
c	Queens Park

6.11
d	Renton

6.12
c	2–0

6.13
a	Motherwell

6.14
a	Airdrie

6.15
c	Montrose

6.16
d	Cowdenbeath

6.17
d	The Spiders

6.18
b	The Beanos

6.19
d	The Blue

6.20
b	The Loons

6.21
b	Alloa

6.22
c	Sparta Prague

6.23
b	Big Jim Holton

6.24
c	Ayr United

6.25
a	Queen of the South

6.26
b	Ally McCoist

6.27
a	Sam English

6.28
b	Jimmy McGrory

6.29
a	The Amsterdam Arena

6.30
a	Philips Stadion

6.31

b	Greenock Abstainers

6.32

c	Stirling Albion

6.33

a	Roy Aitken

6.34

d	Sixpence

6.35

b	Deedle Dawdle

6.36

b	Jinky

6.37

c	John McGinlay

6.38

b	The Ochils

6.39

a	A Bay

6.40

a	A Bog

6.41

c	Tiny Tim

6.42

b	Attilla the Hun

6.43

c	Caesar

6.44

b	Golf – Montrose play at Links Park

6.45

b	Albert Camus

6.46

c	Pittodrie

6.47

a	Tom Forsyth

6.48

c	Whoever takes it

6.49

ALL	All of these

6.50

b	Advocaat

Sport that Isn't Football

7.1
| d | David Duval |

7.2
| a | Mike Campbell-Lamerton |

7.3
| b | Lasse Viren |

7.4
| a | Bob Seagren |

7.5
| b | Gordon Smith |

7.6
| a | They were all against Wales |

7.7
| a | 1973 |

7.8
| a | Eddie Charlton |

7.9
| a | Pole-vaulting |

7.10
| c | Rod Laver |

7.11
| c | Dinamo Kiev |

7.12
| b | Joe Davis |

7.13
| b | Eddie Charlton |

7.14
| b | Derek Wyatt |

7.15
| b | Sandy Carmichael |

7.16
| d | Romania |

7.17
| d | Scotland |

7.18
| d | All of these |

7.19
| d | Franz Ten Bos |

7.20
| b | Brazil |

7.21
| c | Oddjob |

7.22
| a | Harold Sakata |

7.23
| a | Ken Buchanan |

7.24
| a | Juan Pablo Montoya |

7.25
| b | Muhammed Ali |

7.26
| b | Safin |

7.27
| b | Curling |

7.28
| a | Bogside |

7.29
| a | 11 |

7.30
| d | 35 minutes |

7.31

| b | Holland |

7.32

| d | Silver Broom |

7.33

| a | 40 yards |

7.34

| b | The rink |

7.35

| b | 5'8" |

7.36

| a | St Andrews |

7.37

| c | Troon |

7.38

| c | St Lydwina of Schiedam |

7.39

| a | Marbles |

7.40

| b | Never |

7.41

| d | The North |

7.42

| b | Tommy Armour |

7.43

| b | Carnoustie |

7.44

| d | Jim Reeves |

7.45

| b | The Stanley Cup |

7.46

| b | The Calcutta Cup |

7.47

| b | Rugby League |

7.48

| a | Bault |

7.49

| b | Mighty Mouse |

7.50

| b | Jordanhill |

Glaswegians and Food

8.1
| b | 88 |

8.2
| b | Ashton Lane |

8.3
| a | Chips |

8.4
| a | Lamb broth |

8.5
| b | Another name for hairst bree |

8.6
| b | A yeasted roll |

8.7
| d | Chicken and ham |

8.8
| b | Anchovies |

8.9
| c | Currants and raisins |

8.10
| d | A kind of grass |

8.11
| a | Seaweed |

8.12
| d | A thin slice of meat |

8.13
| b | A cream crowdie |

8.14
| b | Triangular bits of shortbread |

8.15
| c | A kind of chicken soup |

8.16
| c | Small cakes |

8.17
| c | Aberdeen rolls |

8.18
| b | Biscuits |

8.19
| c | Sugar |

8.20
| b | Smoked ham and poached fish |

8.21
| b | Fruit cake |

8.22
| b | Gingerbread |

8.23
| a | A heated mixture of beer and whisky |

8.24
| d | Chicken |

8.25
| d | Fish |

8.26
| a | Fruit loaf |

8.27
| b | Oatmeal |

8.28
| c | Anchovies |

8.29
| c | A dessert |

8.30
| a | Whisky |

8.31

b	A sponge cake

8.32

b	Small cod

8.33

b	Pancakes

8.34

a	Thick fish soup

8.35

b	A turkey

8.36

b	Salmon

8.37

a	Theevil

8.38

d	Porridge

8.39

c	Mull

8.40

d	A mixture of grains

8.41

c	Beggars

8.42

a	A mixture of grains

8.43

b	Potatoes and cabbage

8.44

b	Potatoes and turnip

8.45

a	In the oven

8.46

c	Sponge

8.47

c	An oatmeal dumpling

8.48

d	A made-up word

8.49

b	Oblomov's

8.50

c	A Glasgow hotel/restaurant/pub

Architecture, Geography and a Bit More History

9.1

a   Union Street and Argyle Street

9.2

c   Nelson Mandela Place

9.3

b   1807

9.4

c   William Stark

9.5

c   Sir Walter Scott

9.6

a   He asked for this in his will

9.7

c   William Stark

9.8

c   High Street

9.9

a   1794

9.10

b   Joseph Lister

9.11

b   Castle Street

9.12

c   13th

9.13

a   603 AD

9.14

c   St Mungo's Museum

9.15

c   Sauchiehall Street

9.16

a   The Beresford Hotel

9.17

d   Art Deco

9.18

c   Student accommodation

9.19

b   Renfrew Street

9.20

c   London

9.21

c   Cancer

9.22

d   Art Nouveau

9.23

a   Berkley Street

9.24

a   Stephen Mitchell

9.25

b   Andrew Carnegie

9.26

c   Govan Cross

9.27

c   A sailing ship

9.28

b   Sir William Pearce

9.29

b   Fairfields

9.30

a   Despair

9.31

a	Sir J. J. Burnet

9.32

a	A grocer's in the Trongate

9.33

c	Shettleston Road

9.34

a	1717

9.35

d	Parkhead

9.36

a	Glasgow

9.37

c	Loch Katrine

9.38

b	Saltmarket

9.39

c	Cardonald

9.40

a	1950

9.41

d	Cathedral Square

9.42

a	Westminster Abbey

9.43

b	George Street

9.44

c	Place of the Badger

9.45

a	Beautiful Town

9.46

c	God's Garden

9.47

ALL	No, No, No and No

9.48

c	St Andrews Cross

9.49

a	Beardmore's

9.50

c	Robert Adam

The Clyde, Ships and Socialism

10.1

b	'The hammers' ding-dong'

10.2

a	Near Moffatt

10.3

a	Around 70

10.4

a	Scott's of Greenock

10.5

b	*Vulcan*

10.6

a	Faskine

10.7

b	*The Fairy Queen*

10.8

a	Steam

10.9

a	1834

10.10

a	1834

10.11

b	Riveters

10.12

c	Shipwright

10.13

b	A speedboat

10.14

c	She capsized

10.15

a	124

10.16

a	Fairfields

10.17

c	*Empress of Scotland*

10.18

a	Denny of Dumbarton

10.19

b	The Forth

10.20

a	*Robert the Bruce*

10.21

a	Denny of Dumbarton

10.22

d	Barclay Curle

10.23

c	John Brown's

10.24

b	736

10.25

c	1967

10.26

d	Alfred

10.27

b	Robert

10.28

b	A. & J. Inglis

10.29

a	1947

10.30

b	Drunk

10.31

a	Kvaerner Govan Ltd

10.32

a	*Queen Mary*

10.33

c	Hong Kong

10.34

b	80 per cent

10.35

b	54 hours

10.36

b	America

10.37

b	Black

10.38

a	Black, red waterline

10.39

d	Blue, black top

10.40

b	Black, red waterline

10.41

b	*Britannia*

10.42

b	Charles Dickens

10.43

a	The jiners and hauders-on

10.44

a	1931

10.45

c	1934

10.46

b	Over 3000

10.47

a	Three

10.48

d	There was none

10.49

b	The Black Gang

10.50

a	Per rivet

How Did You Do?

Score	Extremely non-mathematical percentages	Verdict
510–460	100–90%	Careful, your pants may be on fire.
459–355	89–70%	You are a trivia genius on Glasgow. Walk up to anyone, no matter your accent, and say, 'I am a Glaswegian!' You've earned it and you can prove it.
354–255	69–50%	You know more about Glasgow than most of its citizens. Give yourself a pat on the back – and a mick as well if you have Irish antecedents.
254–155	49–30%	You are probably from Motherwell and trying very hard, as Motherwell people do. Or maybe Kilsyth.
154–50	29–10%	How are things in Edinburgh, now that you've moved there from Aberdeen or vice versa?
49–0	9–0%	You are English and we know you are. Do not attempt to escape. Your genetic profile has betrayed you. Resistance is futile.